The Caregiver's Journal for Avoiding Burnout

TONYA SPITLER

Maitland, Florida

Published 2023 by Orange Blossom Publishing
Maitland, Florida
www.orangeblossombooks.com

ISBN: 978-1-949935-66-0

THIS JOURNAL BELONGS TO:

....

YEAR:

....

<u>Resources:</u>

Family Caregiver Alliance
National Center on Caregiving
(415) 434-3388 | (800) 445-8106
Website: www.caregiver.org
Email: info@caregiver.org
FCA CareNav: fca.cacrc.org
Services by State: www.caregiver.org/connecting-caregivers/services-by-state/

A Note from Tonya

Choosing to become a caregiver for a loved one is a very personal decision. Whether you are a short-term or long-term caregiver, it is important to take care of **you** as well. Often caregivers put themselves last. Making time to care for yourself in the midst of doctor's appointments, medication administration, and basic needs of your loved one can seem daunting.

Joy can get lost in the midst of day-to-day struggles. Refocusing relationships, with not only your loved one, but friends and family as well as with yourself, can help to alleviate stress and burnout. Caregiver is one piece of the puzzle that is you. Throughout this journal, you will find opportunities to reflect and focus on the pieces of you that exist outside of the caregiver role.

While it is easier to put our own needs to the side, it is essential to ensure we are in the best health physically and mentally. We must first care for ourselves before we can care for others. According to Family Caregiver Alliance, studies have shown higher rates of depression and mental health problems in caregivers versus their same age non-caregiver peers.

Providing care, while different in every situation, places demands on the caregiver in ways that are unique to any other situation. Depending on the level of care required, this can quickly become a full-time experience. Being prepared, and having systems in place to care for yourself as well as your loved one, are so important.

Watching my grandmother care for her mother throughout her dementia journey was inspiring. Through the rapid decline of my great-grandmother's mental state, my grandmother provided the best care she was able at all times. However, she did not do this alone. Her siblings and children helped provide respite care and support when she needed it most. When the needs of my great-grandmother became too much, a sibling stepped in and cared for her until ultimately her care required a facility.

When my mother was undergoing cancer treatments, my sister stepped in to be her primary caregiver. Attending appointments, administering medications, ensuring my mother ate well, and was cared for became her ultimate focus. However, again, she did not do it alone. My aunt and I stepped in to provide respite care and assist with appointments, emotional support, and more.

These experiences have driven home how essential it is for a caregiver to have support as well. No one can go it alone forever. Reaching out to others and allowing them to help is difficult for many, however it is pivotal for long-term success.

This journal is filled with tips and tricks to help you focus on caring for yourself while caring for someone else. Caregivers can feel isolated, lonely, overwhelmed, and exhausted. It is my hope you will find strength and encouragement in these pages.

Tonya

INTRODUCTORY REFLECTION QUESTIONS

Why did I choose to be a caregiver?

....

....

....

....

What is my goal in becoming the caregiver for my loved one?

....

....

....

....

What support groups are available in my area?

....

....

....

....

What support groups have I identified online?

....

....

....

....

INTRODUCTORY REFLECTION QUESTIONS

My plan to maintain my physical and mental health includes:

....

....

....

....

My support system of friends and family are......... and can help by..........

....

....

....

....

Things I can do to help mitigate stress:

....

....

....

....

....

....

....

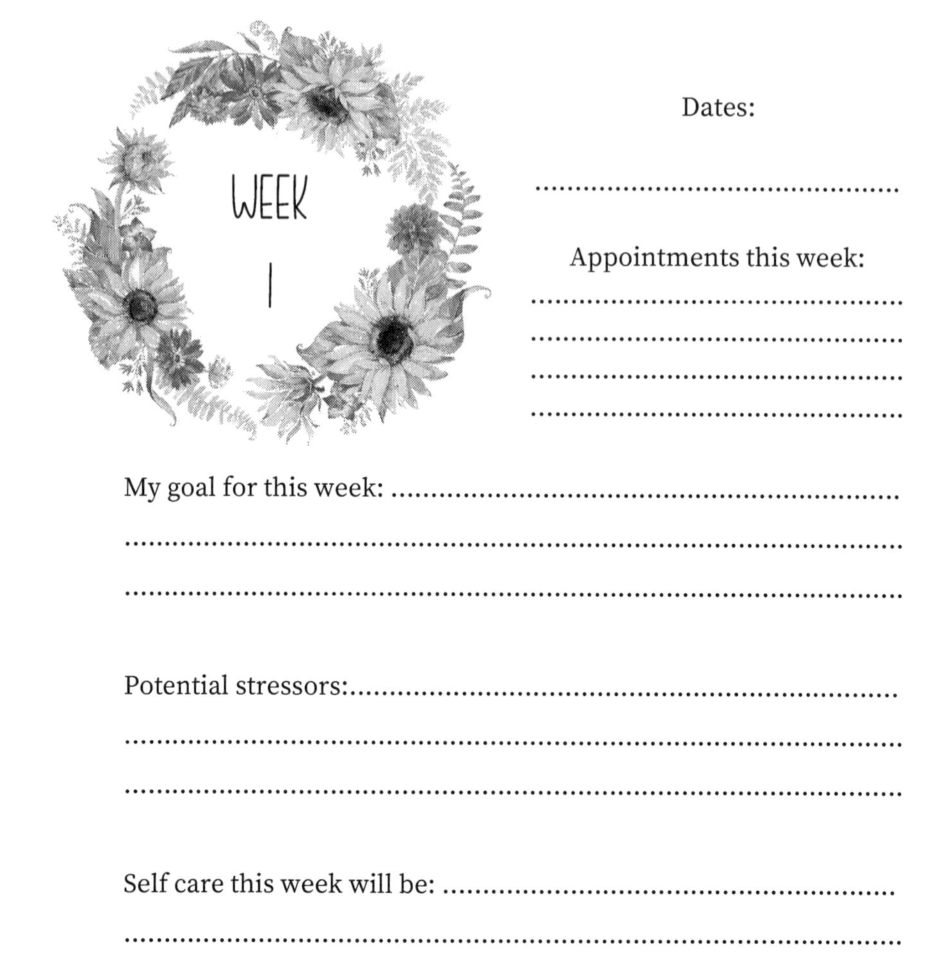

Dates:

....

Appointments this week:

....

....

....

....

My goal for this week: ....

....

....

Potential stressors:..

....

....

Self care this week will be: ....

....

....

Plan for including physical fitness: ....

....

....

Plan for healthy eating: ....

....

....

Hobbies or interests I will pursue this week: ....

....

This week, I plan to reach out to: ....

....

Sleep goal: .... hours each night

Monday

I slept	I ate (circle)	I spent
hours	1 2 3 healthy meals	minutes on self care or hobbies
I reached out to	Today I feel/felt	Today's positive moment

Tuesday

I slept	I ate (circle)	I spent
hours	1 2 3 healthy meals	minutes on self care or hobbies
I reached out to	Today I feel/felt	Today's positive moment

Wednesday

I slept	I ate (circle)	I spent
hours	1 2 3 healthy meals	minutes on self care or hobbies

I reached out to	Today I feel/felt	Today's positive moment

Thursday

I slept	I ate (circle)	I spent
hours	1 2 3 healthy meals	minutes on self care or hobbies

I reached out to	Today I feel/felt	Today's positive moment

Friday

I slept	I ate (circle)	I spent
hours	1 2 3 healthy meals	minutes on self care or hobbies

I reached out to	Today I feel/felt	Today's positive moment

Saturday

I slept	I ate (circle)	I spent
hours	1 2 3 healthy meals	minutes on self care or hobbies
I reached out to	Today I feel/felt	Today's positive moment

Sunday

I slept	I ate (circle)	I spent
hours	1 2 3 healthy meals	minutes on self care or hobbies
I reached out to	Today I feel/felt	Today's positive moment

WEEKLY REFLECTION

How did you do this week with taking care of yourself?

....

....

....

....

....

....

Dates:

....

Appointments this week:

....

....

....

....

My goal for this week: ....

....

....

Potential stressors:..

....

....

Self care this week will be: ....

....

....

Plan for including physical fitness: ....

....

....

Plan for healthy eating: ....

....

....

Hobbies or interests I will pursue this week: ....

....

This week, I plan to reach out to: ....

....

Sleep goal: .... hours each night

Monday

I slept	I ate (circle)	I spent
hours	1 2 3 healthy meals	minutes on self care or hobbies
I reached out to	Today I feel/felt	Today's positive moment

Tuesday

I slept	I ate (circle)	I spent
hours	1 2 3 healthy meals	minutes on self care or hobbies
I reached out to	Today I feel/felt	Today's positive moment

Wednesday

I slept	I ate (circle)	I spent
hours	1 2 3 healthy meals	minutes on self care or hobbies
I reached out to	Today I feel/felt	Today's positive moment

Thursday

I slept	I ate (circle)	I spent
hours	1 2 3 healthy meals	minutes on self care or hobbies
I reached out to	Today I feel/felt	Today's positive moment

Friday

I slept	I ate (circle)	I spent
hours	1 2 3 healthy meals	minutes on self care or hobbies
I reached out to	Today I feel/felt	Today's positive moment

Saturday

I slept	I ate (circle)	I spent
hours	1 2 3 healthy meals	minutes on self care or hobbies
I reached out to	Today I feel/felt	Today's positive moment

Sunday

I slept	I ate (circle)	I spent
hours	1 2 3 healthy meals	minutes on self care or hobbies
I reached out to	Today I feel/felt	Today's positive moment

WEEKLY REFLECTION

How did you do this week with taking care of yourself?

....

....

....

....

....

....

Dates:

....

Appointments this week:

....

....

....

....

My goal for this week: ....

....

....

Potential stressors:...

....

....

Self care this week will be: ....

....

....

Plan for including physical fitness: ....

....

....

Plan for healthy eating: ....

....

....

Hobbies or interests I will pursue this week: ....

....

This week, I plan to reach out to: ....

....

Sleep goal: .... hours each night

Monday

I slept	I ate (circle)	I spent
hours	1 2 3 healthy meals	minutes on self care or hobbies
I reached out to	Today I feel/felt	Today's positive moment

Tuesday

I slept	I ate (circle)	I spent
hours	1 2 3 healthy meals	minutes on self care or hobbies
I reached out to	Today I feel/felt	Today's positive moment

Wednesday

I slept	I ate (circle)	I spent
hours	1 2 3 healthy meals	minutes on self care or hobbies
I reached out to	**Today I feel/felt**	**Today's positive moment**

Thursday

I slept	I ate (circle)	I spent
hours	1 2 3 healthy meals	minutes on self care or hobbies
I reached out to	**Today I feel/felt**	**Today's positive moment**

Friday

I slept	I ate (circle)	I spent
hours	1 2 3 healthy meals	minutes on self care or hobbies
I reached out to	**Today I feel/felt**	**Today's positive moment**

Saturday

I slept	I ate (circle)	I spent
hours	1 2 3 healthy meals	minutes on self care or hobbies
I reached out to	Today I feel/felt	Today's positive moment

Sunday

I slept	I ate (circle)	I spent
hours	1 2 3 healthy meals	minutes on self care or hobbies
I reached out to	Today I feel/felt	Today's positive moment

WEEKLY REFLECTION

How did you do this week with taking care of yourself?

....

....

....

....

....

....

Dates:

....

Appointments this week:

....

....

....

....

My goal for this week: ....

....

....

Potential stressors:..

....

....

Self care this week will be: ....

....

....

Plan for including physical fitness: ....

....

....

Plan for healthy eating: ....

....

....

Hobbies or interests I will pursue this week: ....

....

This week, I plan to reach out to: ....

....

Sleep goal: .... hours each night

Monday

I slept hours	I ate (circle) 1 2 3 healthy meals	I spent minutes on self care or hobbies
I reached out to	Today I feel/felt	Today's positive moment

Tuesday

I slept hours	I ate (circle) 1 2 3 healthy meals	I spent minutes on self care or hobbies
I reached out to	Today I feel/felt	Today's positive moment

Wednesday

I slept	I ate (circle)	I spent
hours	1 2 3 healthy meals	minutes on self care or hobbies
I reached out to	Today I feel/felt	Today's positive moment

Thursday

I slept	I ate (circle)	I spent
hours	1 2 3 healthy meals	minutes on self care or hobbies
I reached out to	Today I feel/felt	Today's positive moment

Friday

I slept	I ate (circle)	I spent
hours	1 2 3 healthy meals	minutes on self care or hobbies
I reached out to	Today I feel/felt	Today's positive moment

Saturday

I slept	I ate (circle)	I spent
hours	1 2 3 healthy meals	minutes on self care or hobbies
I reached out to	Today I feel/felt	Today's positive moment

Sunday

I slept	I ate (circle)	I spent
hours	1 2 3 healthy meals	minutes on self care or hobbies
I reached out to	Today I feel/felt	Today's positive moment

WEEKLY REFLECTION

How did you do this week with taking care of yourself?

....

....

....

....

....

....

MONTHY REFLECTION

I was/was not able to meet my main goal this month because:

....

....

....

The schedule I set for myself was helpful/ needs work and I will:

....

....

....

This month I spent time taking care of my physical health by:

....

....

I feel my sleep habits were:

....

....

My diet this month can be best described as:

....

....

This month, my self-care looked like:

....

....

....

This month, I reached out to:

....

....

This month, I made time to rest and enjoy my hobbies by:

....

....

....

The most stressful moment of the month was:

....

....

....

The best memory of the month was:

....

....

....

....

....

....

Who am I outside of being a caregiver?

....

....

....

....

....

....

....

....

....

....

....

....

....

....

....

....

....

....

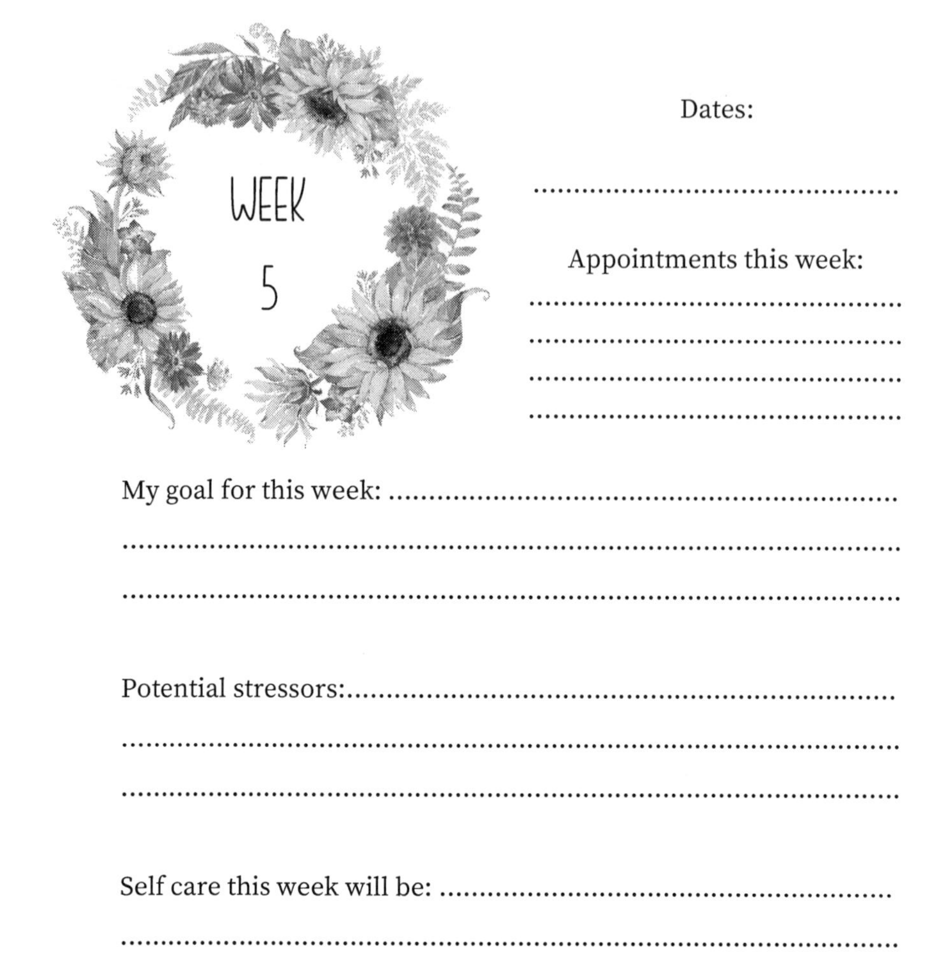

Dates:

....

Appointments this week:

....

....

....

....

My goal for this week: ....

....

....

Potential stressors: ....

....

....

Self care this week will be: ....

....

....

Plan for including physical fitness: ....

....

....

Plan for healthy eating: ....

....

....

Hobbies or interests I will pursue this week: ....

....

This week, I plan to reach out to: ....

....

Sleep goal: .... hours each night

Monday

I slept hours	I ate (circle) 1 2 3 healthy meals	I spent minutes on self care or hobbies
I reached out to	Today I feel/felt	Today's positive moment

Tuesday

I slept hours	I ate (circle) 1 2 3 healthy meals	I spent minutes on self care or hobbies
I reached out to	Today I feel/felt	Today's positive moment

Wednesday

I slept	I ate (circle)	I spent
hours	1 2 3 healthy meals	minutes on self care or hobbies
I reached out to	Today I feel/felt	Today's positive moment

Thursday

I slept	I ate (circle)	I spent
hours	1 2 3 healthy meals	minutes on self care or hobbies
I reached out to	Today I feel/felt	Today's positive moment

Friday

I slept	I ate (circle)	I spent
hours	1 2 3 healthy meals	minutes on self care or hobbies
I reached out to	Today I feel/felt	Today's positive moment

Saturday

I slept	I ate (circle)	I spent
hours	1 2 3 healthy meals	minutes on self care or hobbies
I reached out to	Today I feel/felt	Today's positive moment

Sunday

I slept	I ate (circle)	I spent
hours	1 2 3 healthy meals	minutes on self care or hobbies
I reached out to	Today I feel/felt	Today's positive moment

WEEKLY REFLECTION

How did you do this week with taking care of yourself?

....

....

....

....

....

....

Dates:

....

Appointments this week:

....

....

....

....

My goal for this week: ....

....

....

Potential stressors:...

....

....

Self care this week will be: ....

....

....

Plan for including physical fitness: ....

....

....

Plan for healthy eating: ....

....

....

Hobbies or interests I will pursue this week: ....

....

This week, I plan to reach out to: ....

....

Sleep goal: .... hours each night

Monday

I slept	I ate (circle)	I spent
hours	1 2 3 healthy meals	minutes on self care or hobbies
I reached out to	Today I feel/felt	Today's positive moment

Tuesday

I slept	I ate (circle)	I spent
hours	1 2 3 healthy meals	minutes on self care or hobbies
I reached out to	Today I feel/felt	Today's positive moment

Wednesday

I slept	I ate (circle)	I spent
hours	1 2 3 healthy meals	minutes on self care or hobbies
I reached out to	Today I feel/felt	Today's positive moment

Thursday

I slept	I ate (circle)	I spent
hours	1 2 3 healthy meals	minutes on self care or hobbies
I reached out to	Today I feel/felt	Today's positive moment

Friday

I slept	I ate (circle)	I spent
hours	1 2 3 healthy meals	minutes on self care or hobbies
I reached out to	Today I feel/felt	Today's positive moment

Saturday

I slept	I ate (circle)	I spent
hours	1 2 3 healthy meals	minutes on self care or hobbies
I reached out to	Today I feel/felt	Today's positive moment

Sunday

I slept	I ate (circle)	I spent
hours	1 2 3 healthy meals	minutes on self care or hobbies
I reached out to	Today I feel/felt	Today's positive moment

WEEKLY REFLECTION

How did you do this week with taking care of yourself?

....

....

....

....

....

....

Dates:

....

Appointments this week:

....

....

....

....

My goal for this week: ....

....

....

Potential stressors: ....

....

....

Self care this week will be: ....

....

....

Plan for including physical fitness: ....

....

....

Plan for healthy eating: ....

....

....

Hobbies or interests I will pursue this week: ....

....

This week, I plan to reach out to: ....

....

Sleep goal: .... hours each night

Monday

I slept hours	I ate (circle) 1 2 3 healthy meals	I spent minutes on self care or hobbies
I reached out to	Today I feel/felt	Today's positive moment

Tuesday

I slept hours	I ate (circle) 1 2 3 healthy meals	I spent minutes on self care or hobbies
I reached out to	Today I feel/felt	Today's positive moment

Wednesday

I slept	I ate (circle)	I spent
hours	1 2 3 healthy meals	minutes on self care or hobbies
I reached out to	Today I feel/felt	Today's positive moment

Thursday

I slept	I ate (circle)	I spent
hours	1 2 3 healthy meals	minutes on self care or hobbies
I reached out to	Today I feel/felt	Today's positive moment

Friday

I slept	I ate (circle)	I spent
hours	1 2 3 healthy meals	minutes on self care or hobbies
I reached out to	Today I feel/felt	Today's positive moment

Saturday

I slept	I ate (circle)	I spent
hours	1 2 3 healthy meals	minutes on self care or hobbies
I reached out to	Today I feel/felt	Today's positive moment

Sunday

I slept	I ate (circle)	I spent
hours	1 2 3 healthy meals	minutes on self care or hobbies
I reached out to	Today I feel/felt	Today's positive moment

WEEKLY REFLECTION

How did you do this week with taking care of yourself?

....

....

....

....

....

....

Dates:

Appointments this week:

My goal for this week:

Potential stressors:

Self care this week will be:

Plan for including physical fitness:

Plan for healthy eating:

Hobbies or interests I will pursue this week: ....

....

This week, I plan to reach out to: ....

....

Sleep goal: .... hours each night

Monday

I slept	I ate (circle)	I spent
hours	1 2 3 healthy meals	minutes on self care or hobbies
I reached out to	Today I feel/felt	Today's positive moment

Tuesday

I slept	I ate (circle)	I spent
hours	1 2 3 healthy meals	minutes on self care or hobbies
I reached out to	Today I feel/felt	Today's positive moment

Wednesday

I slept	I ate (circle)	I spent
hours	1 2 3 healthy meals	minutes on self care or hobbies
I reached out to	Today I feel/felt	Today's positive moment

Thursday

I slept	I ate (circle)	I spent
hours	1 2 3 healthy meals	minutes on self care or hobbies
I reached out to	Today I feel/felt	Today's positive moment

Friday

I slept	I ate (circle)	I spent
hours	1 2 3 healthy meals	minutes on self care or hobbies
I reached out to	Today I feel/felt	Today's positive moment

Saturday

I slept	I ate (circle)	I spent
hours	1 2 3 healthy meals	minutes on self care or hobbies
I reached out to	Today I feel/felt	Today's positive moment

Sunday

I slept	I ate (circle)	I spent
hours	1 2 3 healthy meals	minutes on self care or hobbies
I reached out to	Today I feel/felt	Today's positive moment

WEEKLY REFLECTION

How did you do this week with taking care of yourself?

....

....

....

....

....

....

MONTHY REFLECTION

I was/was not able to meet my main goal this month because:

....

....

....

The schedule I set for myself was helpful/ needs work and I will:

....

....

....

This month I spent time taking care of my physical health by:

....

....

I feel my sleep habits were:

....

....

My diet this month can be best described as:

....

....

This month, my self-care looked like:

....

....

....

This month, I reached out to:

....

....

This month, I made time to rest and enjoy my hobbies by:

....

....

....

The most stressful moment of the month was:

....

....

....

The best memory of the month was:

....

....

....

....

....

....

Having outside hobbies and interests is essential for your own mental and emotional health. What is a hobby you are interested in learning more about, and what is a way you can achieve that goal?

....

....

....

....

....

....

....

....

....

....

....

....

....

....

....

Dates:

Appointments this week:

My goal for this week:

Potential stressors:

Self care this week will be:

Plan for including physical fitness:

Plan for healthy eating:

Hobbies or interests I will pursue this week: ....

....

This week, I plan to reach out to: ....

....

Sleep goal: .... hours each night

Monday

I slept	I ate (circle)	I spent
hours	1 2 3 healthy meals	minutes on self care or hobbies
I reached out to	Today I feel/felt	Today's positive moment

Tuesday

I slept	I ate (circle)	I spent
hours	1 2 3 healthy meals	minutes on self care or hobbies
I reached out to	Today I feel/felt	Today's positive moment

Wednesday

I slept	I ate (circle)	I spent
hours	1 2 3 healthy meals	minutes on self care or hobbies
I reached out to	Today I feel/felt	Today's positive moment

Thursday

I slept	I ate (circle)	I spent
hours	1 2 3 healthy meals	minutes on self care or hobbies
I reached out to	Today I feel/felt	Today's positive moment

Friday

I slept	I ate (circle)	I spent
hours	1 2 3 healthy meals	minutes on self care or hobbies
I reached out to	Today I feel/felt	Today's positive moment

Saturday

I slept	I ate (circle)	I spent
hours	1 2 3 healthy meals	minutes on self care or hobbies
I reached out to	Today I feel/felt	Today's positive moment

Sunday

I slept	I ate (circle)	I spent
hours	1 2 3 healthy meals	minutes on self care or hobbies
I reached out to	Today I feel/felt	Today's positive moment

WEEKLY REFLECTION

How did you do this week with taking care of yourself?

....

....

....

....

....

....

Dates:

....

Appointments this week:

....

....

....

....

My goal for this week: ....

....

....

Potential stressors: ....

....

....

Self care this week will be: ....

....

....

Plan for including physical fitness: ....

....

....

Plan for healthy eating: ....

....

....

Hobbies or interests I will pursue this week: ....

....

This week, I plan to reach out to: ....

....

Sleep goal: .... hours each night

Monday

I slept	I ate (circle)	I spent
hours	1 2 3 healthy meals	minutes on self care or hobbies
I reached out to	Today I feel/felt	Today's positive moment

Tuesday

I slept	I ate (circle)	I spent
hours	1 2 3 healthy meals	minutes on self care or hobbies
I reached out to	Today I feel/felt	Today's positive moment

Wednesday

I slept	I ate (circle)	I spent
hours	1 2 3 healthy meals	minutes on self care or hobbies

I reached out to	Today I feel/felt	Today's positive moment

Thursday

I slept	I ate (circle)	I spent
hours	1 2 3 healthy meals	minutes on self care or hobbies

I reached out to	Today I feel/felt	Today's positive moment

Friday

I slept	I ate (circle)	I spent
hours	1 2 3 healthy meals	minutes on self care or hobbies

I reached out to	Today I feel/felt	Today's positive moment

Saturday

I slept	I ate (circle)	I spent
hours	1 2 3 healthy meals	minutes on self care or hobbies
I reached out to	Today I feel/felt	Today's positive moment

Sunday

I slept	I ate (circle)	I spent
hours	1 2 3 healthy meals	minutes on self care or hobbies
I reached out to	Today I feel/felt	Today's positive moment

WEEKLY REFLECTION

How did you do this week with taking care of yourself?

....

....

....

....

....

....

Dates:

....

Appointments this week:

....

....

....

....

My goal for this week: ....

....

....

Potential stressors: ....

....

....

Self care this week will be: ....

....

....

Plan for including physical fitness: ....

....

....

Plan for healthy eating: ....

....

....

Hobbies or interests I will pursue this week: ....

....

This week, I plan to reach out to: ....

....

Sleep goal: .... hours each night

Monday

I slept	I ate (circle)	I spent
hours	1 2 3 healthy meals	minutes on self care or hobbies
I reached out to	Today I feel/felt	Today's positive moment

Tuesday

I slept	I ate (circle)	I spent
hours	1 2 3 healthy meals	minutes on self care or hobbies
I reached out to	Today I feel/felt	Today's positive moment

Wednesday

I slept	I ate (circle)	I spent
hours	1 2 3 healthy meals	minutes on self care or hobbies
I reached out to	Today I feel/felt	Today's positive moment

Thursday

I slept	I ate (circle)	I spent
hours	1 2 3 healthy meals	minutes on self care or hobbies
I reached out to	Today I feel/felt	Today's positive moment

Friday

I slept	I ate (circle)	I spent
hours	1 2 3 healthy meals	minutes on self care or hobbies
I reached out to	Today I feel/felt	Today's positive moment

Saturday

I slept	I ate (circle)	I spent
hours	1 2 3 healthy meals	minutes on self care or hobbies
I reached out to	Today I feel/felt	Today's positive moment

Sunday

I slept	I ate (circle)	I spent
hours	1 2 3 healthy meals	minutes on self care or hobbies
I reached out to	Today I feel/felt	Today's positive moment

WEEKLY REFLECTION

How did you do this week with taking care of yourself?

....

....

....

....

....

....

Dates:

....

Appointments this week:

....
....
....
....

My goal for this week: ....

....

....

Potential stressors:..

....

....

Self care this week will be: ....

....

....

Plan for including physical fitness: ....

....

....

Plan for healthy eating: ....

....

....

Hobbies or interests I will pursue this week: ....

....

This week, I plan to reach out to: ....

....

Sleep goal: .... hours each night

Monday

I slept hours	I ate (circle) 1 2 3 healthy meals	I spent minutes on self care or hobbies
I reached out to	Today I feel/felt	Today's positive moment

Tuesday

I slept hours	I ate (circle) 1 2 3 healthy meals	I spent minutes on self care or hobbies
I reached out to	Today I feel/felt	Today's positive moment

Wednesday

I slept	I ate (circle)	I spent
hours	1 2 3 healthy meals	minutes on self care or hobbies
I reached out to	Today I feel/felt	Today's positive moment

Thursday

I slept	I ate (circle)	I spent
hours	1 2 3 healthy meals	minutes on self care or hobbies
I reached out to	Today I feel/felt	Today's positive moment

Friday

I slept	I ate (circle)	I spent
hours	1 2 3 healthy meals	minutes on self care or hobbies
I reached out to	Today I feel/felt	Today's positive moment

Saturday

I slept	I ate (circle)	I spent
hours	1 2 3 healthy meals	minutes on self care or hobbies
I reached out to	Today I feel/felt	Today's positive moment

Sunday

I slept	I ate (circle)	I spent
hours	1 2 3 healthy meals	minutes on self care or hobbies
I reached out to	Today I feel/felt	Today's positive moment

WEEKLY REFLECTION

How did you do this week with taking care of yourself?

....

....

....

....

....

....

MONTHY REFLECTION

I was/was not able to meet my main goal this month because:

....

....

....

The schedule I set for myself was helpful/ needs work and I will:

....

....

....

This month I spent time taking care of my physical health by:

....

....

I feel my sleep habits were:

....

....

My diet this month can be best described as:

....

....

This month, my self-care looked like:

....

....

....

This month, I reached out to:

....

....

This month, I made time to rest and enjoy my hobbies by:

....

....

....

The most stressful moment of the month was:

....

....

....

The best memory of the month was:

....

....

....

....

....

....

Self-care is easily overlooked. Identify eight ways you can indulge in self-care throughout the year.

Dates:

....

Appointments this week:

....

....

....

....

My goal for this week: ....

....

....

Potential stressors:...

....

....

Self care this week will be: ....

....

....

Plan for including physical fitness: ....

....

....

Plan for healthy eating: ....

....

....

Hobbies or interests I will pursue this week: ....

....

This week, I plan to reach out to: ....

....

Sleep goal: .... hours each night

Monday

I slept hours	I ate (circle) 1 2 3 healthy meals	I spent minutes on self care or hobbies
I reached out to	Today I feel/felt	Today's positive moment

Tuesday

I slept hours	I ate (circle) 1 2 3 healthy meals	I spent minutes on self care or hobbies
I reached out to	Today I feel/felt	Today's positive moment

Wednesday

I slept	I ate (circle)	I spent
hours	1 2 3 healthy meals	minutes on self care or hobbies
I reached out to	Today I feel/felt	Today's positive moment

Thursday

I slept	I ate (circle)	I spent
hours	1 2 3 healthy meals	minutes on self care or hobbies
I reached out to	Today I feel/felt	Today's positive moment

Friday

I slept	I ate (circle)	I spent
hours	1 2 3 healthy meals	minutes on self care or hobbies
I reached out to	Today I feel/felt	Today's positive moment

Saturday

I slept hours	I ate (circle) 1 2 3 healthy meals	I spent minutes on self care or hobbies
I reached out to	Today I feel/felt	Today's positive moment

Sunday

I slept hours	I ate (circle) 1 2 3 healthy meals	I spent minutes on self care or hobbies
I reached out to	Today I feel/felt	Today's positive moment

WEEKLY REFLECTION

How did you do this week with taking care of yourself?

....

....

....

....

....

....

Dates:

....

Appointments this week:

....

....

....

....

My goal for this week: ....

....

....

Potential stressors:..

....

....

Self care this week will be: ....

....

....

Plan for including physical fitness: ....

....

....

Plan for healthy eating: ....

....

....

Hobbies or interests I will pursue this week: ....

....

This week, I plan to reach out to: ....

....

Sleep goal: .... hours each night

Monday

I slept	I ate (circle)	I spent
hours	1 2 3 healthy meals	minutes on self care or hobbies
I reached out to	Today I feel/felt	Today's positive moment

Tuesday

I slept	I ate (circle)	I spent
hours	1 2 3 healthy meals	minutes on self care or hobbies
I reached out to	Today I feel/felt	Today's positive moment

Wednesday

I slept	I ate (circle)	I spent
hours	1 2 3 healthy meals	minutes on self care or hobbies
I reached out to	Today I feel/felt	Today's positive moment

Thursday

I slept	I ate (circle)	I spent
hours	1 2 3 healthy meals	minutes on self care or hobbies
I reached out to	Today I feel/felt	Today's positive moment

Friday

I slept	I ate (circle)	I spent
hours	1 2 3 healthy meals	minutes on self care or hobbies
I reached out to	Today I feel/felt	Today's positive moment

Saturday

I slept	I ate (circle)	I spent
hours	1 2 3 healthy meals	minutes on self care or hobbies
I reached out to	Today I feel/felt	Today's positive moment

Sunday

I slept	I ate (circle)	I spent
hours	1 2 3 healthy meals	minutes on self care or hobbies
I reached out to	Today I feel/felt	Today's positive moment

WEEKLY REFLECTION

How did you do this week with taking care of yourself?

....

....

....

....

....

....

Dates:

....

Appointments this week:

....

....

....

....

My goal for this week: ....

....

....

Potential stressors: ....

....

....

Self care this week will be: ....

....

....

Plan for including physical fitness: ....

....

....

Plan for healthy eating: ....

....

....

Hobbies or interests I will pursue this week: ....

....

This week, I plan to reach out to: ....

....

Sleep goal: .... hours each night

Monday

I slept	I ate (circle)	I spent
hours	1 2 3 healthy meals	minutes on self care or hobbies
I reached out to	Today I feel/felt	Today's positive moment

Tuesday

I slept	I ate (circle)	I spent
hours	1 2 3 healthy meals	minutes on self care or hobbies
I reached out to	Today I feel/felt	Today's positive moment

Wednesday

I slept	I ate (circle)	I spent
hours	1 2 3 healthy meals	minutes on self care or hobbies
I reached out to	Today I feel/felt	Today's positive moment

Thursday

I slept	I ate (circle)	I spent
hours	1 2 3 healthy meals	minutes on self care or hobbies
I reached out to	Today I feel/felt	Today's positive moment

Friday

I slept	I ate (circle)	I spent
hours	1 2 3 healthy meals	minutes on self care or hobbies
I reached out to	Today I feel/felt	Today's positive moment

Saturday

I slept	I ate (circle)	I spent
hours	1 2 3 healthy meals	minutes on self care or hobbies
I reached out to	Today I feel/felt	Today's positive moment

Sunday

I slept	I ate (circle)	I spent
hours	1 2 3 healthy meals	minutes on self care or hobbies
I reached out to	Today I feel/felt	Today's positive moment

WEEKLY REFLECTION

How did you do this week with taking care of yourself?

....

....

....

....

....

....

Dates:

....

Appointments this week:

....

....

....

....

My goal for this week: ....

....

....

Potential stressors: ....

....

....

Self care this week will be: ....

....

....

Plan for including physical fitness: ....

....

....

Plan for healthy eating: ....

....

....

Hobbies or interests I will pursue this week: ....

....

This week, I plan to reach out to: ....

....

Sleep goal: .... hours each night

Monday

I slept	I ate (circle)	I spent
hours	1 2 3 healthy meals	minutes on self care or hobbies
I reached out to	Today I feel/felt	Today's positive moment

Tuesday

I slept	I ate (circle)	I spent
hours	1 2 3 healthy meals	minutes on self care or hobbies
I reached out to	Today I feel/felt	Today's positive moment

Wednesday

I slept	I ate (circle)	I spent
hours	1 2 3 healthy meals	minutes on self care or hobbies
I reached out to	Today I feel/felt	Today's positive moment

Thursday

I slept	I ate (circle)	I spent
hours	1 2 3 healthy meals	minutes on self care or hobbies
I reached out to	Today I feel/felt	Today's positive moment

Friday

I slept	I ate (circle)	I spent
hours	1 2 3 healthy meals	minutes on self care or hobbies
I reached out to	Today I feel/felt	Today's positive moment

Saturday

I slept	I ate (circle)	I spent
hours	1 2 3 healthy meals	minutes on self care or hobbies
I reached out to	Today I feel/felt	Today's positive moment

Sunday

I slept	I ate (circle)	I spent
hours	1 2 3 healthy meals	minutes on self care or hobbies
I reached out to	Today I feel/felt	Today's positive moment

WEEKLY REFLECTION

How did you do this week with taking care of yourself?

....

....

....

....

....

....

MONTHY REFLECTION

I was/was not able to meet my main goal this month because:

....

....

....

The schedule I set for myself was helpful/ needs work and I will:

....

....

....

This month I spent time taking care of my physical health by:

....

....

I feel my sleep habits were:

....

....

My diet this month can be best described as:

....

....

This month, my self-care looked like:

....

....

....

This month, I reached out to:

....

....

This month, I made time to rest and enjoy my hobbies by:

....

....

....

The most stressful moment of the month was:

....

....

....

The best memory of the month was:

....

....

....

....

....

....

Sleep is fundamental in maintaining your physical and mental health. Tips to help you get a restful night's sleep:

Setting a sleep schedule can help you by allowing your body rhythms to set a sleep/wake cycle. Being consistent will help you feel more rested overall. What is your ideal bedtime?............
Your ideal wake time?....................

Avoid heavy meals and caffeine too close to bedtime. Discomfort from being overfull or the stimulant effect of too much caffeine is sure to disrupt your sleep. What changes can you make to your diet to help you get a better night's sleep?

....

....

....

Include physical activity in your day. Taking a walk, scheduling some time in the gym, or doing your favorite at-home workout not only helps keep your body physically fit, but helps to clear your mind, boost your mood, and encourages good sleeping habits. What is your favorite way to include some physical activity into your day?

....

....

....

Create a bedtime routine. This can include journaling, meditation, a skincare routine, a bubble bath, setting the temperature a bit lower, and more. What would you like to include in your bedtime routine?

....

....

....

Find ways to help calm your mind. Some examples might be soothing music, aroma therapy, guided meditation, or progressive muscle relaxation. Which methods of relaxation and calm will you try?

....

....

....

Keep a sleep diary. Mark down the time you went to bed, and when you woke up. Take note of how you slept, how you felt upon waking up. Take it a step further by noting how you felt throughout the day. Reflect below and turn the page for a full sleep diary.

....

....

....

....

....

....

....

....

....

SLEEP DIARY

Bedtime:	Wakeup time:	How I Slept:	How I Felt Waking:	How I Felt During the Day

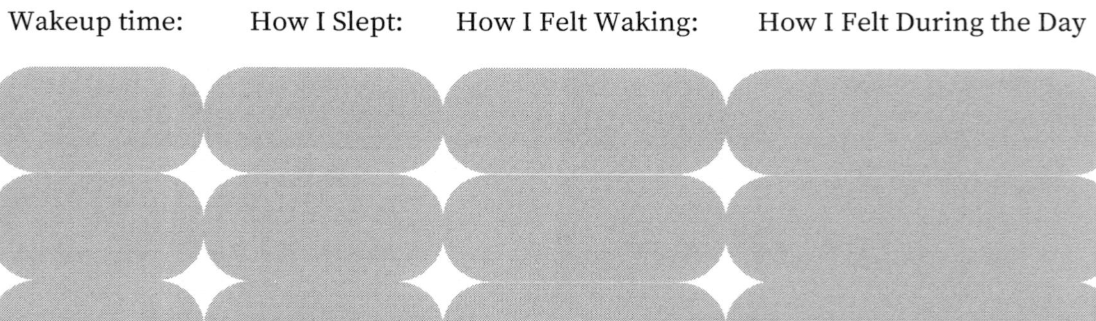

SLEEP DIARY

Bedtime:	Wakeup time:	How I Slept:	How I Felt Waking:	How I Felt During the Day

Dates:

....

Appointments this week:

....

....

....

....

My goal for this week: ....

....

....

Potential stressors:..

....

....

Self care this week will be: ....

....

....

Plan for including physical fitness: ....

....

....

Plan for healthy eating: ....

....

....

Hobbies or interests I will pursue this week: ....

....

This week, I plan to reach out to: ....

....

Sleep goal: .... hours each night

Monday

I slept hours	I ate (circle) 1 2 3 healthy meals	I spent minutes on self care or hobbies
I reached out to	Today I feel/felt	Today's positive moment

Tuesday

I slept hours	I ate (circle) 1 2 3 healthy meals	I spent minutes on self care or hobbies
I reached out to	Today I feel/felt	Today's positive moment

Wednesday

I slept	I ate (circle)	I spent
hours	1 2 3 healthy meals	minutes on self care or hobbies
I reached out to	Today I feel/felt	Today's positive moment

Thursday

I slept	I ate (circle)	I spent
hours	1 2 3 healthy meals	minutes on self care or hobbies
I reached out to	Today I feel/felt	Today's positive moment

Friday

I slept	I ate (circle)	I spent
hours	1 2 3 healthy meals	minutes on self care or hobbies
I reached out to	Today I feel/felt	Today's positive moment

Saturday

I slept	I ate (circle)	I spent
hours	1 2 3 healthy meals	minutes on self care or hobbies
I reached out to	Today I feel/felt	Today's positive moment

Sunday

I slept	I ate (circle)	I spent
hours	1 2 3 healthy meals	minutes on self care or hobbies
I reached out to	Today I feel/felt	Today's positive moment

WEEKLY REFLECTION

How did you do this week with taking care of yourself?

....

....

....

....

....

....

Dates:

....

Appointments this week:

....

....

....

....

My goal for this week: ....

....

....

Potential stressors:..

....

....

Self care this week will be: ....

....

....

Plan for including physical fitness: ....

....

....

Plan for healthy eating: ....

....

....

Hobbies or interests I will pursue this week: ....

....

This week, I plan to reach out to: ....

....

Sleep goal: .... hours each night

Monday

I slept	I ate (circle)	I spent
hours	1 2 3 healthy meals	minutes on self care or hobbies
I reached out to	Today I feel/felt	Today's positive moment

Tuesday

I slept	I ate (circle)	I spent
hours	1 2 3 healthy meals	minutes on self care or hobbies
I reached out to	Today I feel/felt	Today's positive moment

Wednesday

I slept	I ate (circle)	I spent
hours	1 2 3 healthy meals	minutes on self care or hobbies
I reached out to	Today I feel/felt	Today's positive moment

Thursday

I slept	I ate (circle)	I spent
hours	1 2 3 healthy meals	minutes on self care or hobbies
I reached out to	Today I feel/felt	Today's positive moment

Friday

I slept	I ate (circle)	I spent
hours	1 2 3 healthy meals	minutes on self care or hobbies
I reached out to	Today I feel/felt	Today's positive moment

Saturday

I slept	I ate (circle)	I spent
hours	1 2 3 healthy meals	minutes on self care or hobbies
I reached out to	Today I feel/felt	Today's positive moment

Sunday

I slept	I ate (circle)	I spent
hours	1 2 3 healthy meals	minutes on self care or hobbies
I reached out to	Today I feel/felt	Today's positive moment

WEEKLY REFLECTION

How did you do this week with taking care of yourself?

....

....

....

....

....

....

Dates:

....

Appointments this week:

....

....

....

....

My goal for this week: ....

....

....

Potential stressors: ....

....

....

Self care this week will be: ....

....

....

Plan for including physical fitness: ....

....

....

Plan for healthy eating: ....

....

....

Hobbies or interests I will pursue this week: ....

....

This week, I plan to reach out to: ....

....

Sleep goal: .... hours each night

Monday

I slept hours	I ate (circle) 1 2 3 healthy meals	I spent minutes on self care or hobbies
I reached out to	Today I feel/felt	Today's positive moment

Tuesday

I slept hours	I ate (circle) 1 2 3 healthy meals	I spent minutes on self care or hobbies
I reached out to	Today I feel/felt	Today's positive moment

Wednesday

I slept	I ate (circle)	I spent
hours	1 2 3 healthy meals	minutes on self care or hobbies
I reached out to	Today I feel/felt	Today's positive moment

Thursday

I slept	I ate (circle)	I spent
hours	1 2 3 healthy meals	minutes on self care or hobbies
I reached out to	Today I feel/felt	Today's positive moment

Friday

I slept	I ate (circle)	I spent
hours	1 2 3 healthy meals	minutes on self care or hobbies
I reached out to	Today I feel/felt	Today's positive moment

Saturday

I slept	I ate (circle)	I spent
hours	1 2 3 healthy meals	minutes on self care or hobbies
I reached out to	Today I feel/felt	Today's positive moment

Sunday

I slept	I ate (circle)	I spent
hours	1 2 3 healthy meals	minutes on self care or hobbies
I reached out to	Today I feel/felt	Today's positive moment

WEEKLY REFLECTION

How did you do this week with taking care of yourself?

....

....

....

....

....

....

Dates:

....

Appointments this week:

....

....

....

....

My goal for this week: ....

....

....

Potential stressors:..

....

....

Self care this week will be: ....

....

....

Plan for including physical fitness: ....

....

....

Plan for healthy eating: ....

....

....

Hobbies or interests I will pursue this week: ....

....

This week, I plan to reach out to: ....

....

Sleep goal: .... hours each night

Monday

I slept	I ate (circle)	I spent
hours	1 2 3 healthy meals	minutes on self care or hobbies
I reached out to	Today I feel/felt	Today's positive moment

Tuesday

I slept	I ate (circle)	I spent
hours	1 2 3 healthy meals	minutes on self care or hobbies
I reached out to	Today I feel/felt	Today's positive moment

Wednesday

I slept	I ate (circle)	I spent
hours	1 2 3 healthy meals	minutes on self care or hobbies
I reached out to	Today I feel/felt	Today's positive moment

Thursday

I slept	I ate (circle)	I spent
hours	1 2 3 healthy meals	minutes on self care or hobbies
I reached out to	Today I feel/felt	Today's positive moment

Friday

I slept	I ate (circle)	I spent
hours	1 2 3 healthy meals	minutes on self care or hobbies
I reached out to	Today I feel/felt	Today's positive moment

Saturday

I slept	I ate (circle)	I spent
hours	1 2 3 healthy meals	minutes on self care or hobbies
I reached out to	Today I feel/felt	Today's positive moment

Sunday

I slept	I ate (circle)	I spent
hours	1 2 3 healthy meals	minutes on self care or hobbies
I reached out to	Today I feel/felt	Today's positive moment

WEEKLY REFLECTION

How did you do this week with taking care of yourself?

....

....

....

....

....

....

MONTHY REFLECTION

I was/was not able to meet my main goal this month because:

....

....

....

The schedule I set for myself was helpful/ needs work and I will:

....

....

....

This month I spent time taking care of my physical health by:

....

....

I feel my sleep habits were:

....

....

My diet this month can be best described as:

....

....

This month, my self-care looked like:

....

....

....

This month, I reached out to:

....

....

This month, I made time to rest and enjoy my hobbies by:

....

....

....

The most stressful moment of the month was:

....

....

....

The best memory of the month was:

....

....

....

....

....

....

Your own healthcare is important. Yearly appointments such as medical check ups, optometry checks, dental appointments, gynecological check ups, mammograms, etc. are all important to maintaining your own health. If you are not healthy, you won't be able to care for your loved one or yourself. Use the space below to schedule your own health appointments.

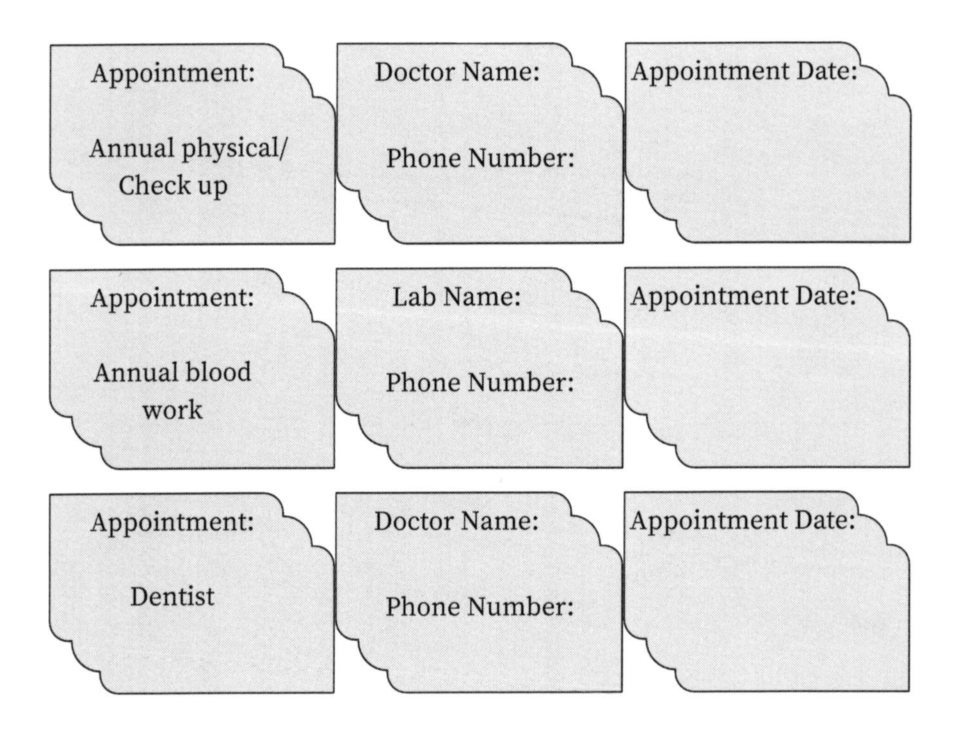

Appointment: Annual physical/ Check up	Doctor Name: Phone Number:	Appointment Date:
Appointment: Annual blood work	Lab Name: Phone Number:	Appointment Date:
Appointment: Dentist	Doctor Name: Phone Number:	Appointment Date:

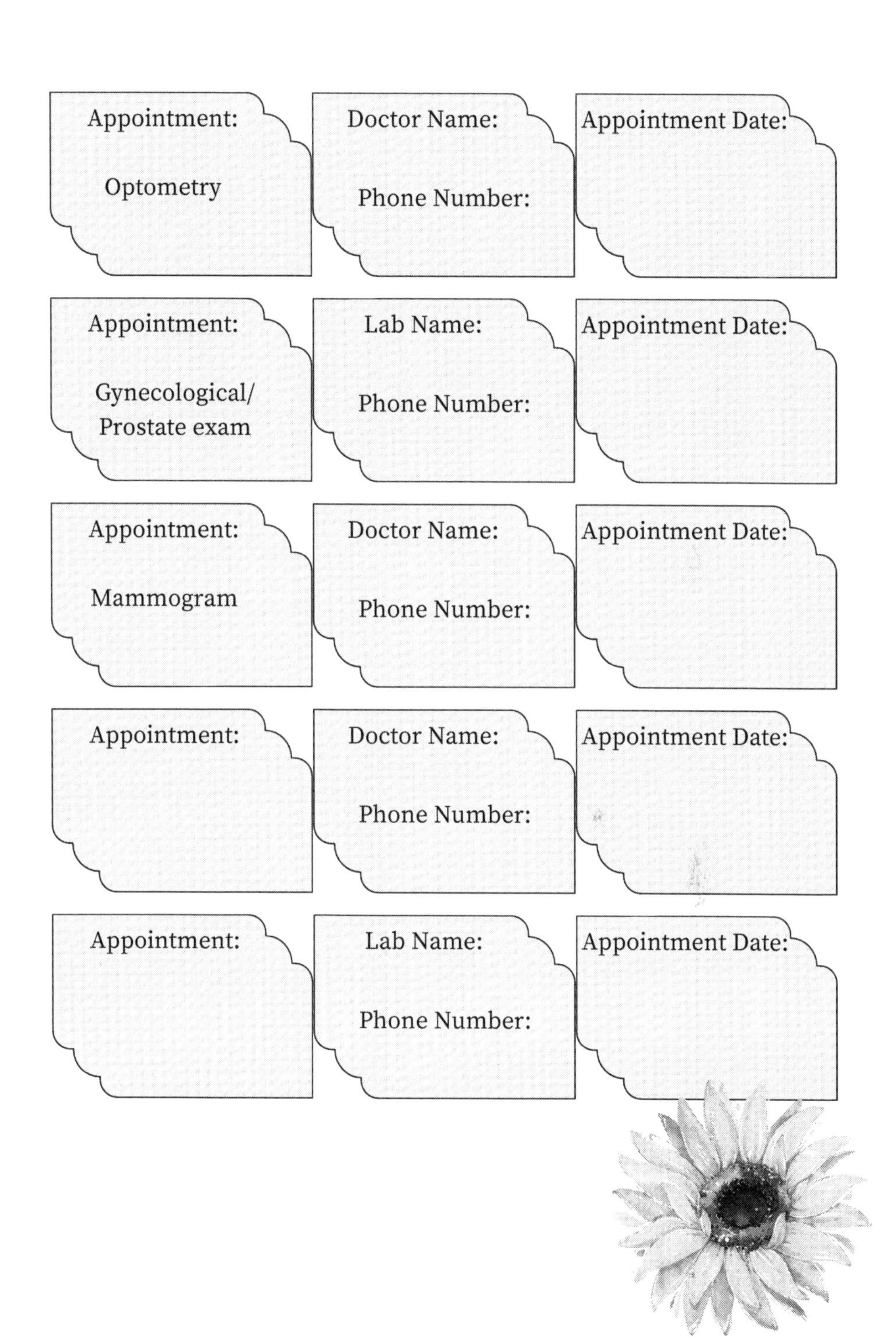

Appointment:	Doctor Name: / Phone Number:	Appointment Date:
Optometry	Doctor Name: Phone Number:	Appointment Date:
Gynecological/ Prostate exam	Lab Name: Phone Number:	Appointment Date:
Mammogram	Doctor Name: Phone Number:	Appointment Date:
Appointment:	Doctor Name: Phone Number:	Appointment Date:
Appointment:	Lab Name: Phone Number:	Appointment Date:

Dates:

....

Appointments this week:

....

....

....

....

My goal for this week: ....

....

....

Potential stressors:...

....

....

Self care this week will be: ....

....

....

Plan for including physical fitness: ....

....

....

Plan for healthy eating: ....

....

....

Hobbies or interests I will pursue this week: ....
....

This week, I plan to reach out to: ....
....

Sleep goal: .... hours each night

Monday

I slept	I ate (circle)	I spent
hours	1 2 3 healthy meals	minutes on self care or hobbies
I reached out to	Today I feel/felt	Today's positive moment

Tuesday

I slept	I ate (circle)	I spent
hours	1 2 3 healthy meals	minutes on self care or hobbies
I reached out to	Today I feel/felt	Today's positive moment

Wednesday

I slept	I ate (circle)	I spent
hours	1 2 3 healthy meals	minutes on self care or hobbies
I reached out to	Today I feel/felt	Today's positive moment

Thursday

I slept	I ate (circle)	I spent
hours	1 2 3 healthy meals	minutes on self care or hobbies
I reached out to	Today I feel/felt	Today's positive moment

Friday

I slept	I ate (circle)	I spent
hours	1 2 3 healthy meals	minutes on self care or hobbies
I reached out to	Today I feel/felt	Today's positive moment

Saturday

I slept	I ate (circle)	I spent
hours	1 2 3 healthy meals	minutes on self care or hobbies
I reached out to	Today I feel/felt	Today's positive moment

Sunday

I slept	I ate (circle)	I spent
hours	1 2 3 healthy meals	minutes on self care or hobbies
I reached out to	Today I feel/felt	Today's positive moment

WEEKLY REFLECTION

How did you do this week with taking care of yourself?

....

....

....

....

....

....

Dates:

....

Appointments this week:

....

....

....

....

My goal for this week: ....

....

....

Potential stressors:..

....

....

Self care this week will be: ....

....

....

Plan for including physical fitness: ....

....

....

Plan for healthy eating: ....

....

....

Hobbies or interests I will pursue this week: ....

....

This week, I plan to reach out to: ....

....

Sleep goal: .... hours each night

Monday

I slept	I ate (circle)	I spent
hours	1 2 3 healthy meals	minutes on self care or hobbies
I reached out to	Today I feel/felt	Today's positive moment

Tuesday

I slept	I ate (circle)	I spent
hours	1 2 3 healthy meals	minutes on self care or hobbies
I reached out to	Today I feel/felt	Today's positive moment

Wednesday

I slept	I ate (circle)	I spent
hours	1 2 3 healthy meals	minutes on self care or hobbies
I reached out to	Today I feel/felt	Today's positive moment

Thursday

I slept	I ate (circle)	I spent
hours	1 2 3 healthy meals	minutes on self care or hobbies
I reached out to	Today I feel/felt	Today's positive moment

Friday

I slept	I ate (circle)	I spent
hours	1 2 3 healthy meals	minutes on self care or hobbies
I reached out to	Today I feel/felt	Today's positive moment

Saturday

I slept	I ate (circle)	I spent
hours	1 2 3 healthy meals	minutes on self care or hobbies
I reached out to	Today I feel/felt	Today's positive moment

Sunday

I slept	I ate (circle)	I spent
hours	1 2 3 healthy meals	minutes on self care or hobbies
I reached out to	Today I feel/felt	Today's positive moment

WEEKLY REFLECTION

How did you do this week with taking care of yourself?

....

....

....

....

....

....

Dates:

....

Appointments this week:

....

....

....

....

My goal for this week: ....

....

....

Potential stressors:..

....

....

Self care this week will be: ....

....

....

Plan for including physical fitness: ....

....

....

Plan for healthy eating: ....

....

....

Hobbies or interests I will pursue this week: ....
....

This week, I plan to reach out to: ....
....

Sleep goal: .... hours each night

Monday

I slept hours	I ate (circle) 1 2 3 healthy meals	I spent minutes on self care or hobbies
I reached out to	Today I feel/felt	Today's positive moment

Tuesday

I slept hours	I ate (circle) 1 2 3 healthy meals	I spent minutes on self care or hobbies
I reached out to	Today I feel/felt	Today's positive moment

Wednesday

I slept	I ate (circle)	I spent
hours	1 2 3 healthy meals	minutes on self care or hobbies
I reached out to	Today I feel/felt	Today's positive moment

Thursday

I slept	I ate (circle)	I spent
hours	1 2 3 healthy meals	minutes on self care or hobbies
I reached out to	Today I feel/felt	Today's positive moment

Friday

I slept	I ate (circle)	I spent
hours	1 2 3 healthy meals	minutes on self care or hobbies
I reached out to	Today I feel/felt	Today's positive moment

Saturday

I slept hours	I ate (circle) 1 2 3 healthy meals	I spent minutes on self care or hobbies
I reached out to	Today I feel/felt	Today's positive moment

Sunday

I slept hours	I ate (circle) 1 2 3 healthy meals	I spent minutes on self care or hobbies
I reached out to	Today I feel/felt	Today's positive moment

WEEKLY REFLECTION

How did you do this week with taking care of yourself?

....

....

....

....

....

....

Dates:

....

Appointments this week:

....

....

....

....

My goal for this week: ....

....

....

Potential stressors: ....

....

....

Self care this week will be: ....

....

....

Plan for including physical fitness: ....

....

....

Plan for healthy eating: ....

....

....

Hobbies or interests I will pursue this week: ....

....

This week, I plan to reach out to: ....

....

Sleep goal: .... hours each night

Monday

I slept	I ate (circle)	I spent
hours	1 2 3 healthy meals	minutes on self care or hobbies
I reached out to	Today I feel/felt	Today's positive moment

Tuesday

I slept	I ate (circle)	I spent
hours	1 2 3 healthy meals	minutes on self care or hobbies
I reached out to	Today I feel/felt	Today's positive moment

Wednesday

I slept	I ate (circle)	I spent
hours	1 2 3 healthy meals	minutes on self care or hobbies
I reached out to	Today I feel/felt	Today's positive moment

Thursday

I slept	I ate (circle)	I spent
hours	1 2 3 healthy meals	minutes on self care or hobbies
I reached out to	Today I feel/felt	Today's positive moment

Friday

I slept	I ate (circle)	I spent
hours	1 2 3 healthy meals	minutes on self care or hobbies
I reached out to	Today I feel/felt	Today's positive moment

Saturday

I slept	I ate (circle)	I spent
hours	1 2 3 healthy meals	minutes on self care or hobbies
I reached out to	Today I feel/felt	Today's positive moment

Sunday

I slept	I ate (circle)	I spent
hours	1 2 3 healthy meals	minutes on self care or hobbies
I reached out to	Today I feel/felt	Today's positive moment

WEEKLY REFLECTION

How did you do this week with taking care of yourself?

....

....

....

....

....

....

MONTHY REFLECTION

I was/was not able to meet my main goal this month because:

....

....

....

The schedule I set for myself was helpful/ needs work and I will:

....

....

....

This month I spent time taking care of my physical health by:

....

....

I feel my sleep habits were:

....

....

My diet this month can be best described as:

....

....

This month, my self-care looked like:

....

....

....

This month, I reached out to:

....

....

This month, I made time to rest and enjoy my hobbies by:

....

....

....

The most stressful moment of the month was:

....

....

....

The best memory of the month was:

....

....

....

....

....

....

Being a caregiver can often feel overwhelming. Taking time for yourself is essential. Identify people and services that can offer you a break on a regular basis. Identify those you can call for support in an emergency.

Community Respite Care Services	Phone	Availability
....	....	....
....	....	....
....	....	....

Friends/Family	Phone	Availability
....	....	....
....	....	....
....	....	....

Other	Phone	Availability
....	....	....
....	....	....
....	....	....

My Plan for Getting Help:

Dates:

....

Appointments this week:

....

....

....

....

My goal for this week: ....

....

....

Potential stressors:..

....

....

Self care this week will be: ....

....

....

Plan for including physical fitness: ....

....

....

Plan for healthy eating: ....

....

....

Hobbies or interests I will pursue this week: ....

....

This week, I plan to reach out to: ....

....

Sleep goal: .... hours each night

Monday

I slept	I ate (circle)	I spent
hours	1 2 3 healthy meals	minutes on self care or hobbies
I reached out to	Today I feel/felt	Today's positive moment

Tuesday

I slept	I ate (circle)	I spent
hours	1 2 3 healthy meals	minutes on self care or hobbies
I reached out to	Today I feel/felt	Today's positive moment

Wednesday

I slept hours	I ate (circle) 1 2 3 healthy meals	I spent minutes on self care or hobbies
I reached out to	Today I feel/felt	Today's positive moment

Thursday

I slept hours	I ate (circle) 1 2 3 healthy meals	I spent minutes on self care or hobbies
I reached out to	Today I feel/felt	Today's positive moment

Friday

I slept hours	I ate (circle) 1 2 3 healthy meals	I spent minutes on self care or hobbies
I reached out to	Today I feel/felt	Today's positive moment

Saturday

I slept	I ate (circle)	I spent
hours	1 2 3 healthy meals	minutes on self care or hobbies
I reached out to	Today I feel/felt	Today's positive moment

Sunday

I slept	I ate (circle)	I spent
hours	1 2 3 healthy meals	minutes on self care or hobbies
I reached out to	Today I feel/felt	Today's positive moment

WEEKLY REFLECTION

How did you do this week with taking care of yourself?

....

....

....

....

....

....

Dates:

....

Appointments this week:

....

....

....

....

My goal for this week: ....

....

....

Potential stressors: ....

....

....

Self care this week will be: ....

....

....

Plan for including physical fitness: ....

....

....

Plan for healthy eating: ....

....

....

Hobbies or interests I will pursue this week: ....

....

This week, I plan to reach out to: ....

....

Sleep goal: .... hours each night

Monday

I slept	I ate (circle)	I spent
hours	1 2 3 healthy meals	minutes on self care or hobbies
I reached out to	Today I feel/felt	Today's positive moment

Tuesday

I slept	I ate (circle)	I spent
hours	1 2 3 healthy meals	minutes on self care or hobbies
I reached out to	Today I feel/felt	Today's positive moment

Wednesday

I slept	I ate (circle)	I spent
hours	1 2 3 healthy meals	minutes on self care or hobbies
I reached out to	Today I feel/felt	Today's positive moment

Thursday

I slept	I ate (circle)	I spent
hours	1 2 3 healthy meals	minutes on self care or hobbies
I reached out to	Today I feel/felt	Today's positive moment

Friday

I slept	I ate (circle)	I spent
hours	1 2 3 healthy meals	minutes on self care or hobbies
I reached out to	Today I feel/felt	Today's positive moment

Saturday

I slept	I ate (circle)	I spent
hours	1 2 3 healthy meals	minutes on self care or hobbies
I reached out to	Today I feel/felt	Today's positive moment

Sunday

I slept	I ate (circle)	I spent
hours	1 2 3 healthy meals	minutes on self care or hobbies
I reached out to	Today I feel/felt	Today's positive moment

WEEKLY REFLECTION

How did you do this week with taking care of yourself?

....

....

....

....

....

....

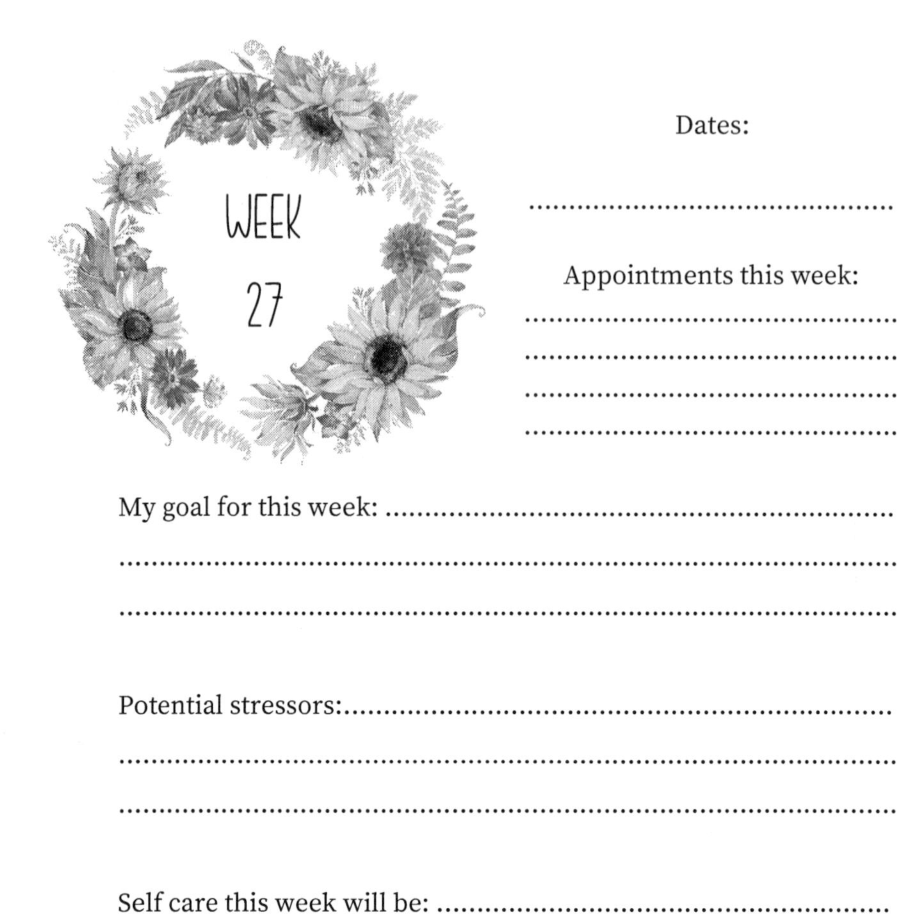

Dates:

....

Appointments this week:

....

....

....

....

My goal for this week: ....

....

....

Potential stressors:...

....

....

Self care this week will be: ....

....

....

Plan for including physical fitness: ....

....

....

Plan for healthy eating: ....

....

....

Hobbies or interests I will pursue this week: ....

....

This week, I plan to reach out to: ....

....

Sleep goal: .... hours each night

Monday

I slept hours	I ate (circle) 1 2 3 healthy meals	I spent minutes on self care or hobbies
I reached out to	Today I feel/felt	Today's positive moment

Tuesday

I slept hours	I ate (circle) 1 2 3 healthy meals	I spent minutes on self care or hobbies
I reached out to	Today I feel/felt	Today's positive moment

Wednesday

I slept	I ate (circle)	I spent
hours	1 2 3 healthy meals	minutes on self care or hobbies
I reached out to	Today I feel/felt	Today's positive moment

Thursday

I slept	I ate (circle)	I spent
hours	1 2 3 healthy meals	minutes on self care or hobbies
I reached out to	Today I feel/felt	Today's positive moment

Friday

I slept	I ate (circle)	I spent
hours	1 2 3 healthy meals	minutes on self care or hobbies
I reached out to	Today I feel/felt	Today's positive moment

Saturday

I slept	I ate (circle)	I spent
hours	1 2 3 healthy meals	minutes on self care or hobbies
I reached out to	Today I feel/felt	Today's positive moment

Sunday

I slept	I ate (circle)	I spent
hours	1 2 3 healthy meals	minutes on self care or hobbies
I reached out to	Today I feel/felt	Today's positive moment

WEEKLY REFLECTION

How did you do this week with taking care of yourself?

....

....

....

....

....

....

Dates:

....

Appointments this week:

....

....

....

....

My goal for this week: ....

....

....

Potential stressors:...

....

....

Self care this week will be: ....

....

....

Plan for including physical fitness: ....

....

....

Plan for healthy eating: ....

....

....

Hobbies or interests I will pursue this week: ....
....

This week, I plan to reach out to: ....
....

Sleep goal: .... hours each night

Monday

I slept	I ate (circle)	I spent
hours	1 2 3 healthy meals	minutes on self care or hobbies
I reached out to	Today I feel/felt	Today's positive moment

Tuesday

I slept	I ate (circle)	I spent
hours	1 2 3 healthy meals	minutes on self care or hobbies
I reached out to	Today I feel/felt	Today's positive moment

Wednesday

I slept	I ate (circle)	I spent
hours	1 2 3 healthy meals	minutes on self care or hobbies
I reached out to	Today I feel/felt	Today's positive moment

Thursday

I slept	I ate (circle)	I spent
hours	1 2 3 healthy meals	minutes on self care or hobbies
I reached out to	Today I feel/felt	Today's positive moment

Friday

I slept	I ate (circle)	I spent
hours	1 2 3 healthy meals	minutes on self care or hobbies
I reached out to	Today I feel/felt	Today's positive moment

Saturday

I slept	I ate (circle)	I spent
hours	1 2 3 healthy meals	minutes on self care or hobbies
I reached out to	Today I feel/felt	Today's positive moment

Sunday

I slept	I ate (circle)	I spent
hours	1 2 3 healthy meals	minutes on self care or hobbies
I reached out to	Today I feel/felt	Today's positive moment

WEEKLY REFLECTION

How did you do this week with taking care of yourself?

....

....

....

....

....

....

MONTHY REFLECTION

I was/was not able to meet my main goal this month because:

....

....

....

The schedule I set for myself was helpful/ needs work and I will:

....

....

....

This month I spent time taking care of my physical health by:

....

....

I feel my sleep habits were:

....

....

My diet this month can be best described as:

....

....

This month, my self-care looked like:

....

....

....

This month, I reached out to:

....

....

This month, I made time to rest and enjoy my hobbies by:

....

....

....

The most stressful moment of the month was:

....

....

....

The best memory of the month was:

....

....

....

....

....

....

Being realistic about the things we can and cannot do is essential. Having a plan in place before you need to make big decisions can help reduce stress and provide clarity. Take a moment to consider what you are able to do and what you are not able to do. What plans can you put in place to assist with the things you are not able to do?

....

....

....

....

Things I am able to do comfortably in the care of my loved one, and what I need to have in place to ensure I am able to continue to provide care are:

....

....

....

....

....

Things I would need assistance with in caring for my loved one are.......... I will find assistance by.........

....

....

....

....

....

Things I absolutely won't be able to do for my loved one are:

....

....

....

....

Consider what will happen if your loved one can no longer toilet independently or requires round-the-clock medical care. If the level of care my loved one needs becomes such that I can no longer provide care, the plan will be to:

....

....

....

....

....

....

....

....

....

Dates:

....

Appointments this week:

....

....

....

....

My goal for this week: ....

....

....

Potential stressors:..

....

....

Self care this week will be: ....

....

....

Plan for including physical fitness: ....

....

....

Plan for healthy eating: ....

....

....

Hobbies or interests I will pursue this week: ....

....

This week, I plan to reach out to: ....

....

Sleep goal: .... hours each night

Monday

I slept	I ate (circle)	I spent
hours	1 2 3 healthy meals	minutes on self care or hobbies
I reached out to	Today I feel/felt	Today's positive moment

Tuesday

I slept	I ate (circle)	I spent
hours	1 2 3 healthy meals	minutes on self care or hobbies
I reached out to	Today I feel/felt	Today's positive moment

Wednesday

I slept	I ate (circle)	I spent
hours	1 2 3 healthy meals	minutes on self care or hobbies
I reached out to	Today I feel/felt	Today's positive moment

Thursday

I slept	I ate (circle)	I spent
hours	1 2 3 healthy meals	minutes on self care or hobbies
I reached out to	Today I feel/felt	Today's positive moment

Friday

I slept	I ate (circle)	I spent
hours	1 2 3 healthy meals	minutes on self care or hobbies
I reached out to	Today I feel/felt	Today's positive moment

Saturday

I slept	I ate (circle)	I spent
hours	1 2 3 healthy meals	minutes on self care or hobbies
I reached out to	Today I feel/felt	Today's positive moment

Sunday

I slept	I ate (circle)	I spent
hours	1 2 3 healthy meals	minutes on self care or hobbies
I reached out to	Today I feel/felt	Today's positive moment

WEEKLY REFLECTION

How did you do this week with taking care of yourself?

....

....

....

....

....

....

Dates:

....

Appointments this week:

....
....
....
....

My goal for this week: ....
....
....

Potential stressors:..
....
....

Self care this week will be: ....
....
....

Plan for including physical fitness: ....
....
....

Plan for healthy eating: ....
....
....

Hobbies or interests I will pursue this week: ....

....

This week, I plan to reach out to: ....

....

Sleep goal: .... hours each night

Monday

I slept hours	I ate (circle) 1 2 3 healthy meals	I spent minutes on self care or hobbies
I reached out to	Today I feel/felt	Today's positive moment

Tuesday

I slept hours	I ate (circle) 1 2 3 healthy meals	I spent minutes on self care or hobbies
I reached out to	Today I feel/felt	Today's positive moment

Wednesday

I slept	I ate (circle)	I spent
hours	1 2 3 healthy meals	minutes on self care or hobbies
I reached out to	Today I feel/felt	Today's positive moment

Thursday

I slept	I ate (circle)	I spent
hours	1 2 3 healthy meals	minutes on self care or hobbies
I reached out to	Today I feel/felt	Today's positive moment

Friday

I slept	I ate (circle)	I spent
hours	1 2 3 healthy meals	minutes on self care or hobbies
I reached out to	Today I feel/felt	Today's positive moment

Saturday

I slept	I ate (circle)	I spent
hours	1 2 3 healthy meals	minutes on self care or hobbies
I reached out to	Today I feel/felt	Today's positive moment

Sunday

I slept	I ate (circle)	I spent
hours	1 2 3 healthy meals	minutes on self care or hobbies
I reached out to	Today I feel/felt	Today's positive moment

WEEKLY REFLECTION

How did you do this week with taking care of yourself?

....

....

....

....

....

....

Dates:

....

Appointments this week:

....

....

....

....

My goal for this week: ....

....

....

Potential stressors: ....

....

....

Self care this week will be: ....

....

....

Plan for including physical fitness: ....

....

....

Plan for healthy eating: ....

....

....

Hobbies or interests I will pursue this week: ....

....

This week, I plan to reach out to: ....

....

Sleep goal: .... hours each night

Monday

I slept	I ate (circle)	I spent
hours	1 2 3 healthy meals	minutes on self care or hobbies
I reached out to	Today I feel/felt	Today's positive moment

Tuesday

I slept	I ate (circle)	I spent
hours	1 2 3 healthy meals	minutes on self care or hobbies
I reached out to	Today I feel/felt	Today's positive moment

Wednesday

I slept	I ate (circle)	I spent
hours	1 2 3 healthy meals	minutes on self care or hobbies
I reached out to	Today I feel/felt	Today's positive moment

Thursday

I slept	I ate (circle)	I spent
hours	1 2 3 healthy meals	minutes on self care or hobbies
I reached out to	Today I feel/felt	Today's positive moment

Friday

I slept	I ate (circle)	I spent
hours	1 2 3 healthy meals	minutes on self care or hobbies
I reached out to	Today I feel/felt	Today's positive moment

Saturday

I slept	I ate (circle)	I spent
hours	1 2 3 healthy meals	minutes on self care or hobbies
I reached out to	Today I feel/felt	Today's positive moment

Sunday

I slept	I ate (circle)	I spent
hours	1 2 3 healthy meals	minutes on self care or hobbies
I reached out to	Today I feel/felt	Today's positive moment

WEEKLY REFLECTION

How did you do this week with taking care of yourself?

....

....

....

....

....

....

Dates:

....

Appointments this week:

....
....
....
....

My goal for this week: ....
....
....

Potential stressors:..
....
....

Self care this week will be: ....
....
....

Plan for including physical fitness: ....
....
....

Plan for healthy eating: ....
....
....

Hobbies or interests I will pursue this week: ....

....

This week, I plan to reach out to: ....

....

Sleep goal: .... hours each night

Monday

I slept	I ate (circle)	I spent
hours	1 2 3 healthy meals	minutes on self care or hobbies

I reached out to	Today I feel/felt	Today's positive moment

Tuesday

I slept	I ate (circle)	I spent
hours	1 2 3 healthy meals	minutes on self care or hobbies

I reached out to	Today I feel/felt	Today's positive moment

Wednesday

I slept	I ate (circle)	I spent
hours	1 2 3 healthy meals	minutes on self care or hobbies
I reached out to	Today I feel/felt	Today's positive moment

Thursday

I slept	I ate (circle)	I spent
hours	1 2 3 healthy meals	minutes on self care or hobbies
I reached out to	Today I feel/felt	Today's positive moment

Friday

I slept	I ate (circle)	I spent
hours	1 2 3 healthy meals	minutes on self care or hobbies
I reached out to	Today I feel/felt	Today's positive moment

Saturday

I slept	I ate (circle)	I spent
hours	1 2 3 healthy meals	minutes on self care or hobbies
I reached out to	Today I feel/felt	Today's positive moment

Sunday

I slept	I ate (circle)	I spent
hours	1 2 3 healthy meals	minutes on self care or hobbies
I reached out to	Today I feel/felt	Today's positive moment

WEEKLY REFLECTION

How did you do this week with taking care of yourself?

....

....

....

....

....

....

MONTHY REFLECTION

I was/was not able to meet my main goal this month because:

....

....

....

The schedule I set for myself was helpful/ needs work and I will:

....

....

....

This month I spent time taking care of my physical health by:

....

....

I feel my sleep habits were:

....

....

My diet this month can be best described as:

....

....

This month, my self-care looked like:

....

....

....

This month, I reached out to:

....

....

This month, I made time to rest and enjoy my hobbies by:

....

....

....

The most stressful moment of the month was:

....

....

....

The best memory of the month was:

....

....

....

....

....

....

As a caregiver, you are facing immense stressors. Between managing appointments, medications, and behaviors, you can often feel overwhelmed. Finding ways to be calm in the midst of the storm is so important. Speaking encouragingly to yourself, including giving yourself grace and forgiveness for negative feelings, is vital.

Things I can do to maintain calm and reduce stress, even in the midst of the hard moments:

....

....

....

....

....

....

....

....

....

....

Encouraging phrases, mantras, or quotes that I can go to during times of stress:

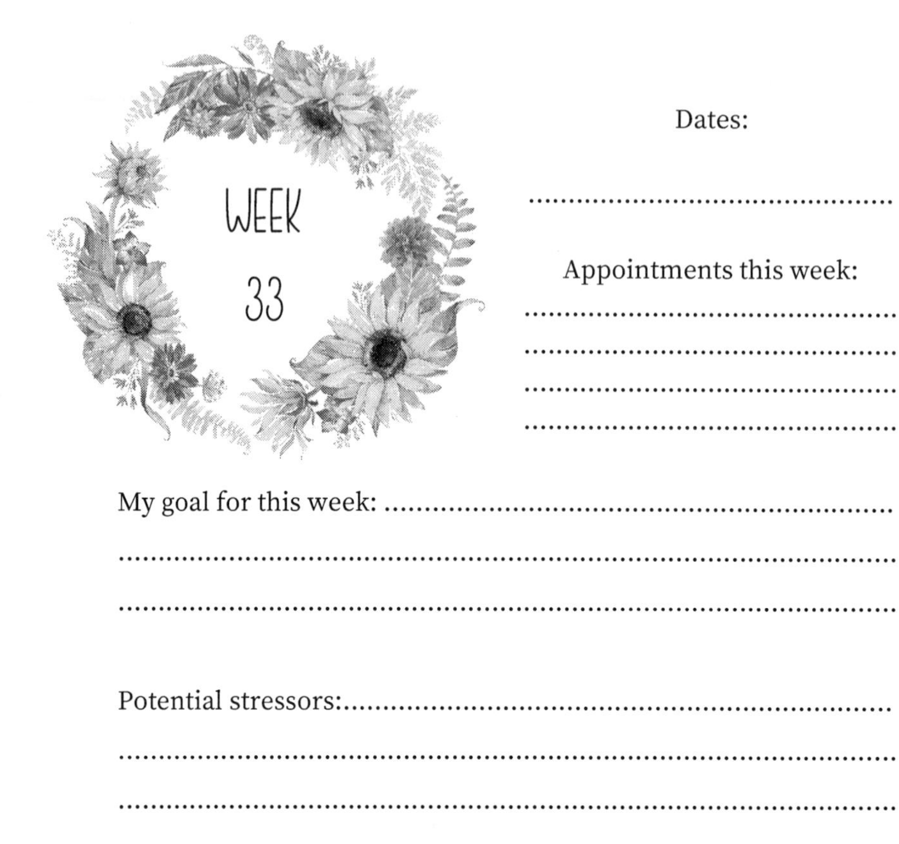

Dates:

....

Appointments this week:

....
....
....
....

My goal for this week: ....

....

....

Potential stressors:..

....

....

Self care this week will be: ....

....

....

Plan for including physical fitness: ....

....

....

Plan for healthy eating: ....

....

....

Hobbies or interests I will pursue this week: ....

....

This week, I plan to reach out to: ....

....

Sleep goal: .... hours each night

Monday

I slept hours	I ate (circle) 1 2 3 healthy meals	I spent minutes on self care or hobbies
I reached out to	Today I feel/felt	Today's positive moment

Tuesday

I slept hours	I ate (circle) 1 2 3 healthy meals	I spent minutes on self care or hobbies
I reached out to	Today I feel/felt	Today's positive moment

Wednesday

I slept	I ate (circle)	I spent
hours	1 2 3 healthy meals	minutes on self care or hobbies
I reached out to	Today I feel/felt	Today's positive moment

Thursday

I slept	I ate (circle)	I spent
hours	1 2 3 healthy meals	minutes on self care or hobbies
I reached out to	Today I feel/felt	Today's positive moment

Friday

I slept	I ate (circle)	I spent
hours	1 2 3 healthy meals	minutes on self care or hobbies
I reached out to	Today I feel/felt	Today's positive moment

Saturday

I slept	I ate (circle)	I spent
hours	1 2 3 healthy meals	minutes on self care or hobbies
I reached out to	Today I feel/felt	Today's positive moment

Sunday

I slept	I ate (circle)	I spent
hours	1 2 3 healthy meals	minutes on self care or hobbies
I reached out to	Today I feel/felt	Today's positive moment

WEEKLY REFLECTION

How did you do this week with taking care of yourself?

....

....

....

....

....

....

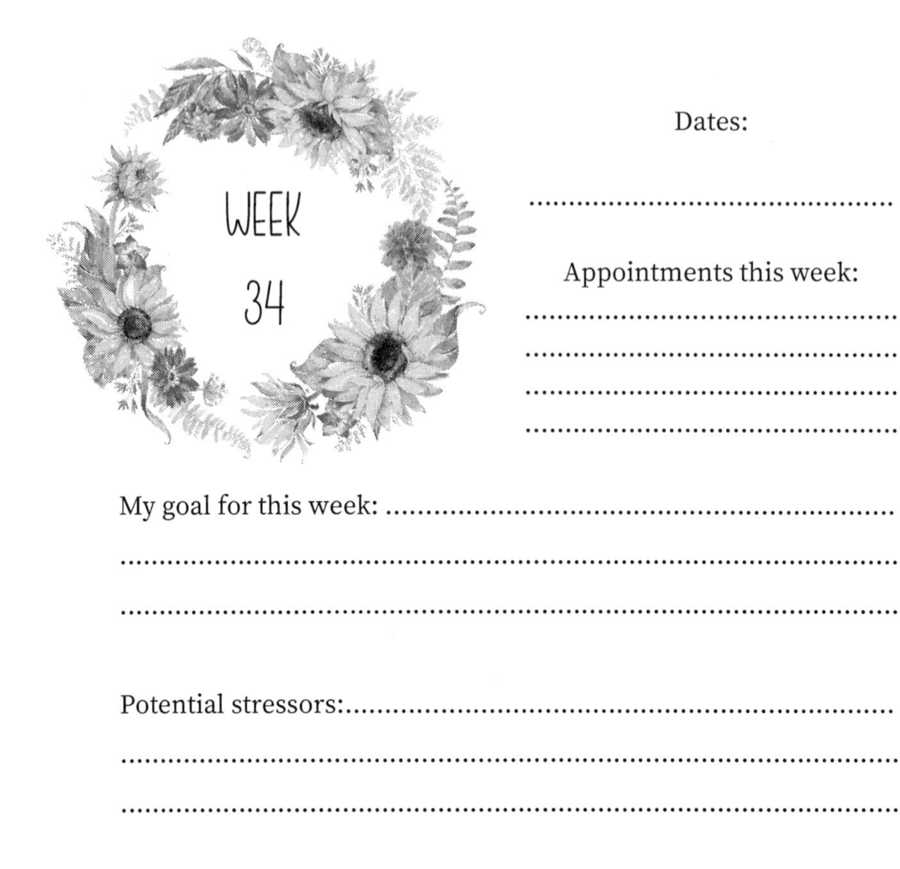

Dates:

....

Appointments this week:

....

....

....

....

My goal for this week: ....

....

....

Potential stressors:...

....

....

Self care this week will be: ....

....

....

Plan for including physical fitness: ....

....

....

Plan for healthy eating: ....

....

....

Hobbies or interests I will pursue this week: ....

....

This week, I plan to reach out to: ....

....

Sleep goal: .... hours each night

Monday

I slept	I ate (circle)	I spent
hours	1 2 3 healthy meals	minutes on self care or hobbies
I reached out to	Today I feel/felt	Today's positive moment

Tuesday

I slept	I ate (circle)	I spent
hours	1 2 3 healthy meals	minutes on self care or hobbies
I reached out to	Today I feel/felt	Today's positive moment

Wednesday

I slept	I ate (circle)	I spent
hours	1 2 3 healthy meals	minutes on self care or hobbies
I reached out to	Today I feel/felt	Today's positive moment

Thursday

I slept	I ate (circle)	I spent
hours	1 2 3 healthy meals	minutes on self care or hobbies
I reached out to	Today I feel/felt	Today's positive moment

Friday

I slept	I ate (circle)	I spent
hours	1 2 3 healthy meals	minutes on self care or hobbies
I reached out to	Today I feel/felt	Today's positive moment

Saturday

I slept	I ate (circle)	I spent
hours	1 2 3 healthy meals	minutes on self care or hobbies
I reached out to	Today I feel/felt	Today's positive moment

Sunday

I slept	I ate (circle)	I spent
hours	1 2 3 healthy meals	minutes on self care or hobbies
I reached out to	Today I feel/felt	Today's positive moment

WEEKLY REFLECTION

How did you do this week with taking care of yourself?

....

....

....

....

....

....

Dates:

....

Appointments this week:

....

....

....

....

My goal for this week: ....

....

....

Potential stressors:...

....

....

Self care this week will be: ....

....

....

Plan for including physical fitness: ....

....

....

Plan for healthy eating: ....

....

....

Hobbies or interests I will pursue this week: ....

....

This week, I plan to reach out to: ....

....

Sleep goal: .... hours each night

Monday

I slept hours	I ate (circle) 1 2 3 healthy meals	I spent minutes on self care or hobbies
I reached out to	Today I feel/felt	Today's positive moment

Tuesday

I slept hours	I ate (circle) 1 2 3 healthy meals	I spent minutes on self care or hobbies
I reached out to	Today I feel/felt	Today's positive moment

Wednesday

I slept	I ate (circle)	I spent
hours	1 2 3 healthy meals	minutes on self care or hobbies
I reached out to	Today I feel/felt	Today's positive moment

Thursday

I slept	I ate (circle)	I spent
hours	1 2 3 healthy meals	minutes on self care or hobbies
I reached out to	Today I feel/felt	Today's positive moment

Friday

I slept	I ate (circle)	I spent
hours	1 2 3 healthy meals	minutes on self care or hobbies
I reached out to	Today I feel/felt	Today's positive moment

Saturday

I slept	I ate (circle)	I spent
hours	1 2 3 healthy meals	minutes on self care or hobbies
I reached out to	Today I feel/felt	Today's positive moment

Sunday

I slept	I ate (circle)	I spent
hours	1 2 3 healthy meals	minutes on self care or hobbies
I reached out to	Today I feel/felt	Today's positive moment

WEEKLY REFLECTION

How did you do this week with taking care of yourself?

....

....

....

....

....

....

Dates:

....

Appointments this week:

....

....

....

....

My goal for this week: ....

....

....

Potential stressors: ....

....

....

Self care this week will be: ....

....

....

Plan for including physical fitness: ....

....

....

Plan for healthy eating: ....

....

....

Hobbies or interests I will pursue this week: ....

....

This week, I plan to reach out to: ....

....

Sleep goal: .... hours each night

Monday

I slept	I ate (circle)	I spent
hours	1 2 3 healthy meals	minutes on self care or hobbies
I reached out to	Today I feel/felt	Today's positive moment

Tuesday

I slept	I ate (circle)	I spent
hours	1 2 3 healthy meals	minutes on self care or hobbies
I reached out to	Today I feel/felt	Today's positive moment

Wednesday

I slept	I ate (circle)	I spent
hours	1 2 3 healthy meals	minutes on self care or hobbies
I reached out to	Today I feel/felt	Today's positive moment

Thursday

I slept	I ate (circle)	I spent
hours	1 2 3 healthy meals	minutes on self care or hobbies
I reached out to	Today I feel/felt	Today's positive moment

Friday

I slept	I ate (circle)	I spent
hours	1 2 3 healthy meals	minutes on self care or hobbies
I reached out to	Today I feel/felt	Today's positive moment

Saturday

I slept	I ate (circle)	I spent
hours	1 2 3 healthy meals	minutes on self care or hobbies
I reached out to	Today I feel/felt	Today's positive moment

Sunday

I slept	I ate (circle)	I spent
hours	1 2 3 healthy meals	minutes on self care or hobbies
I reached out to	Today I feel/felt	Today's positive moment

WEEKLY REFLECTION

How did you do this week with taking care of yourself?

....

....

....

....

....

....

MONTHY REFLECTION

I was/was not able to meet my main goal this month because:

....

....

....

The schedule I set for myself was helpful/ needs work and I will:

....

....

....

This month I spent time taking care of my physical health by:

....

....

I feel my sleep habits were:

....

....

My diet this month can be best described as:

....

....

This month, my self-care looked like:

....

....

....

This month, I reached out to:

....

....

This month, I made time to rest and enjoy my hobbies by:

....

....

....

The most stressful moment of the month was:

....

....

....

The best memory of the month was:

....

....

....

....

....

....

Caring for a loved one can change how you see them in the day to day. It's important to hold onto the memories you have of them prior to their illness or injury. Consider creating a memory board, scrapbook, or picture album that reflects your best memories. Ask your loved one for their favorite memories and include those.

Favorite memories of mine:

....

....

....

....

....

....

....

....

....

....

....

Favorite memories of my loved one:

Dates:

....

Appointments this week:

....

....

....

....

My goal for this week: ....

....

....

Potential stressors:..

....

....

Self care this week will be: ....

....

....

Plan for including physical fitness: ....

....

....

Plan for healthy eating: ....

....

....

Hobbies or interests I will pursue this week: ....

....

This week, I plan to reach out to: ....

....

Sleep goal: .... hours each night

Monday

I slept hours	I ate (circle) 1 2 3 healthy meals	I spent minutes on self care or hobbies
I reached out to	Today I feel/felt	Today's positive moment

Tuesday

I slept hours	I ate (circle) 1 2 3 healthy meals	I spent minutes on self care or hobbies
I reached out to	Today I feel/felt	Today's positive moment

Wednesday

I slept	I ate (circle)	I spent
hours	1 2 3 healthy meals	minutes on self care or hobbies
I reached out to	Today I feel/felt	Today's positive moment

Thursday

I slept	I ate (circle)	I spent
hours	1 2 3 healthy meals	minutes on self care or hobbies
I reached out to	Today I feel/felt	Today's positive moment

Friday

I slept	I ate (circle)	I spent
hours	1 2 3 healthy meals	minutes on self care or hobbies
I reached out to	Today I feel/felt	Today's positive moment

Saturday

I slept hours	I ate (circle) 1 2 3 healthy meals	I spent minutes on self care or hobbies
I reached out to	Today I feel/felt	Today's positive moment

Sunday

I slept hours	I ate (circle) 1 2 3 healthy meals	I spent minutes on self care or hobbies
I reached out to	Today I feel/felt	Today's positive moment

WEEKLY REFLECTION

How did you do this week with taking care of yourself?

....

....

....

....

....

....

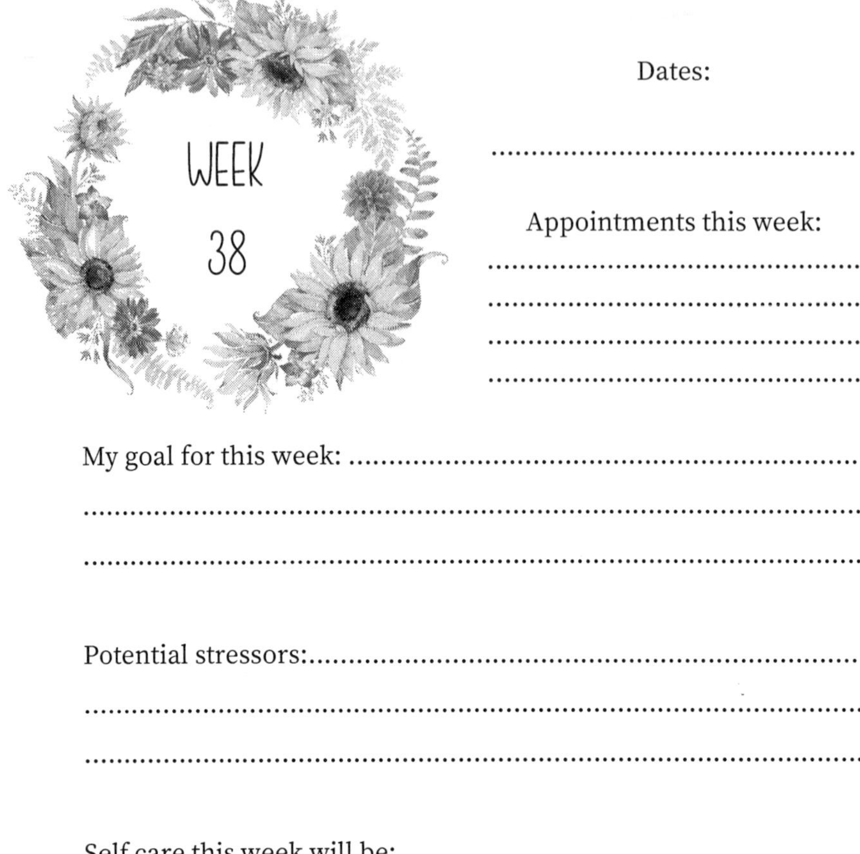

Dates:

....

Appointments this week:

....

....

....

....

My goal for this week: ....

....

....

Potential stressors:..

....

....

Self care this week will be: ....

....

....

Plan for including physical fitness: ....

....

....

Plan for healthy eating: ....

....

....

Hobbies or interests I will pursue this week: ....

....

This week, I plan to reach out to: ....

....

Sleep goal: .... hours each night

Monday

I slept	I ate (circle)	I spent
hours	1 2 3 healthy meals	minutes on self care or hobbies
I reached out to	Today I feel/felt	Today's positive moment

Tuesday

I slept	I ate (circle)	I spent
hours	1 2 3 healthy meals	minutes on self care or hobbies
I reached out to	Today I feel/felt	Today's positive moment

Wednesday

I slept	I ate (circle)	I spent
hours	1 2 3 healthy meals	minutes on self care or hobbies

I reached out to	Today I feel/felt	Today's positive moment

Thursday

I slept	I ate (circle)	I spent
hours	1 2 3 healthy meals	minutes on self care or hobbies

I reached out to	Today I feel/felt	Today's positive moment

Friday

I slept	I ate (circle)	I spent
hours	1 2 3 healthy meals	minutes on self care or hobbies

I reached out to	Today I feel/felt	Today's positive moment

Saturday

I slept	I ate (circle)	I spent
hours	1 2 3 healthy meals	minutes on self care or hobbies
I reached out to	Today I feel/felt	Today's positive moment

Sunday

I slept	I ate (circle)	I spent
hours	1 2 3 healthy meals	minutes on self care or hobbies
I reached out to	Today I feel/felt	Today's positive moment

WEEKLY REFLECTION

How did you do this week with taking care of yourself?

....

....

....

....

....

....

Dates:

....

Appointments this week:

....

....

....

....

My goal for this week: ....

....

....

Potential stressors:..

....

....

Self care this week will be: ....

....

....

Plan for including physical fitness: ....

....

....

Plan for healthy eating: ....

....

....

Hobbies or interests I will pursue this week: ....
....

This week, I plan to reach out to: ....
....

Sleep goal: .... hours each night

Monday

I slept hours	I ate (circle) 1 2 3 healthy meals	I spent minutes on self care or hobbies
I reached out to	Today I feel/felt	Today's positive moment

Tuesday

I slept hours	I ate (circle) 1 2 3 healthy meals	I spent minutes on self care or hobbies
I reached out to	Today I feel/felt	Today's positive moment

Wednesday

I slept	I ate (circle)	I spent
hours	1 2 3 healthy meals	minutes on self care or hobbies
I reached out to	Today I feel/felt	Today's positive moment

Thursday

I slept	I ate (circle)	I spent
hours	1 2 3 healthy meals	minutes on self care or hobbies
I reached out to	Today I feel/felt	Today's positive moment

Friday

I slept	I ate (circle)	I spent
hours	1 2 3 healthy meals	minutes on self care or hobbies
I reached out to	Today I feel/felt	Today's positive moment

Saturday

I slept	I ate (circle)	I spent
hours	1 2 3 healthy meals	minutes on self care or hobbies
I reached out to	Today I feel/felt	Today's positive moment

Sunday

I slept	I ate (circle)	I spent
hours	1 2 3 healthy meals	minutes on self care or hobbies
I reached out to	Today I feel/felt	Today's positive moment

WEEKLY REFLECTION

How did you do this week with taking care of yourself?

....

....

....

....

....

....

Dates:

....

Appointments this week:

....

....

....

....

My goal for this week: ....

....

....

Potential stressors: ....

....

....

Self care this week will be: ....

....

....

Plan for including physical fitness: ....

....

....

Plan for healthy eating: ....

....

....

Hobbies or interests I will pursue this week: ....
....

This week, I plan to reach out to: ....
....

Sleep goal: .... hours each night

Monday

I slept	I ate (circle)	I spent
hours	1 2 3 healthy meals	minutes on self care or hobbies
I reached out to	Today I feel/felt	Today's positive moment

Tuesday

I slept	I ate (circle)	I spent
hours	1 2 3 healthy meals	minutes on self care or hobbies
I reached out to	Today I feel/felt	Today's positive moment

Wednesday

I slept	I ate (circle)	I spent
hours	1 2 3 healthy meals	minutes on self care or hobbies

I reached out to	Today I feel/felt	Today's positive moment

Thursday

I slept	I ate (circle)	I spent
hours	1 2 3 healthy meals	minutes on self care or hobbies

I reached out to	Today I feel/felt	Today's positive moment

Friday

I slept	I ate (circle)	I spent
hours	1 2 3 healthy meals	minutes on self care or hobbies

I reached out to	Today I feel/felt	Today's positive moment

Saturday

I slept	I ate (circle)	I spent
hours	1 2 3 healthy meals	minutes on self care or hobbies
I reached out to	Today I feel/felt	Today's positive moment

Sunday

I slept	I ate (circle)	I spent
hours	1 2 3 healthy meals	minutes on self care or hobbies
I reached out to	Today I feel/felt	Today's positive moment

WEEKLY REFLECTION

How did you do this week with taking care of yourself?

....

....

....

....

....

....

MONTHY REFLECTION

I was/was not able to meet my main goal this month because:

....

....

....

The schedule I set for myself was helpful/ needs work and I will:

....

....

....

This month I spent time taking care of my physical health by:

....

....

I feel my sleep habits were:

....

....

My diet this month can be best described as:

....

....

This month, my self-care looked like:

....

....

....

This month, I reached out to:

....

....

This month, I made time to rest and enjoy my hobbies by:

....

....

....

The most stressful moment of the month was:

....

....

....

The best memory of the month was:

....

....

....

....

....

....

Being a caregiver allows you to spend a lot of time with your loved ones. While this can be sometimes stressful, there are plenty of amazing moments as well. Reflect on your experiences this last month. What are the moments you don't want to forget?

....

....

....

....

....

....

....

....

....

....

....

....

....

....

....

Dates: ....

Appointments this week:

....

....

....

....

My goal for this week: ....

....

....

Potential stressors: ....

....

....

Self care this week will be: ....

....

....

Plan for including physical fitness: ....

....

....

Plan for healthy eating: ....

....

....

Hobbies or interests I will pursue this week: ....

....

This week, I plan to reach out to: ....

....

Sleep goal: .... hours each night

Monday

I slept	I ate (circle)	I spent
hours	1 2 3 healthy meals	minutes on self care or hobbies
I reached out to	Today I feel/felt	Today's positive moment

Tuesday

I slept	I ate (circle)	I spent
hours	1 2 3 healthy meals	minutes on self care or hobbies
I reached out to	Today I feel/felt	Today's positive moment

Wednesday

I slept	I ate (circle)	I spent
hours	1 2 3 healthy meals	minutes on self care or hobbies
I reached out to	Today I feel/felt	Today's positive moment

Thursday

I slept	I ate (circle)	I spent
hours	1 2 3 healthy meals	minutes on self care or hobbies
I reached out to	Today I feel/felt	Today's positive moment

Friday

I slept	I ate (circle)	I spent
hours	1 2 3 healthy meals	minutes on self care or hobbies
I reached out to	Today I feel/felt	Today's positive moment

Saturday

I slept	I ate (circle)	I spent
hours	1 2 3 healthy meals	minutes on self care or hobbies
I reached out to	Today I feel/felt	Today's positive moment

Sunday

I slept	I ate (circle)	I spent
hours	1 2 3 healthy meals	minutes on self care or hobbies
I reached out to	Today I feel/felt	Today's positive moment

WEEKLY REFLECTION

How did you do this week with taking care of yourself?

....

....

....

....

....

....

Dates:

....

Appointments this week:

....

....

....

....

My goal for this week: ....

....

....

Potential stressors:..

....

....

Self care this week will be: ....

....

....

Plan for including physical fitness: ....

....

....

Plan for healthy eating: ....

....

....

Hobbies or interests I will pursue this week: ....

....

This week, I plan to reach out to: ....

....

Sleep goal: .... hours each night

Monday

I slept	I ate (circle)	I spent
hours	1 2 3 healthy meals	minutes on self care or hobbies
I reached out to	Today I feel/felt	Today's positive moment

Tuesday

I slept	I ate (circle)	I spent
hours	1 2 3 healthy meals	minutes on self care or hobbies
I reached out to	Today I feel/felt	Today's positive moment

Wednesday

I slept	I ate (circle)	I spent
hours	1 2 3 healthy meals	minutes on self care or hobbies
I reached out to	Today I feel/felt	Today's positive moment

Thursday

I slept	I ate (circle)	I spent
hours	1 2 3 healthy meals	minutes on self care or hobbies
I reached out to	Today I feel/felt	Today's positive moment

Friday

I slept	I ate (circle)	I spent
hours	1 2 3 healthy meals	minutes on self care or hobbies
I reached out to	Today I feel/felt	Today's positive moment

Saturday

I slept	I ate (circle)	I spent
hours	1 2 3 healthy meals	minutes on self care or hobbies
I reached out to	Today I feel/felt	Today's positive moment

Sunday

I slept	I ate (circle)	I spent
hours	1 2 3 healthy meals	minutes on self care or hobbies
I reached out to	Today I feel/felt	Today's positive moment

WEEKLY REFLECTION

How did you do this week with taking care of yourself?

....

....

....

....

....

....

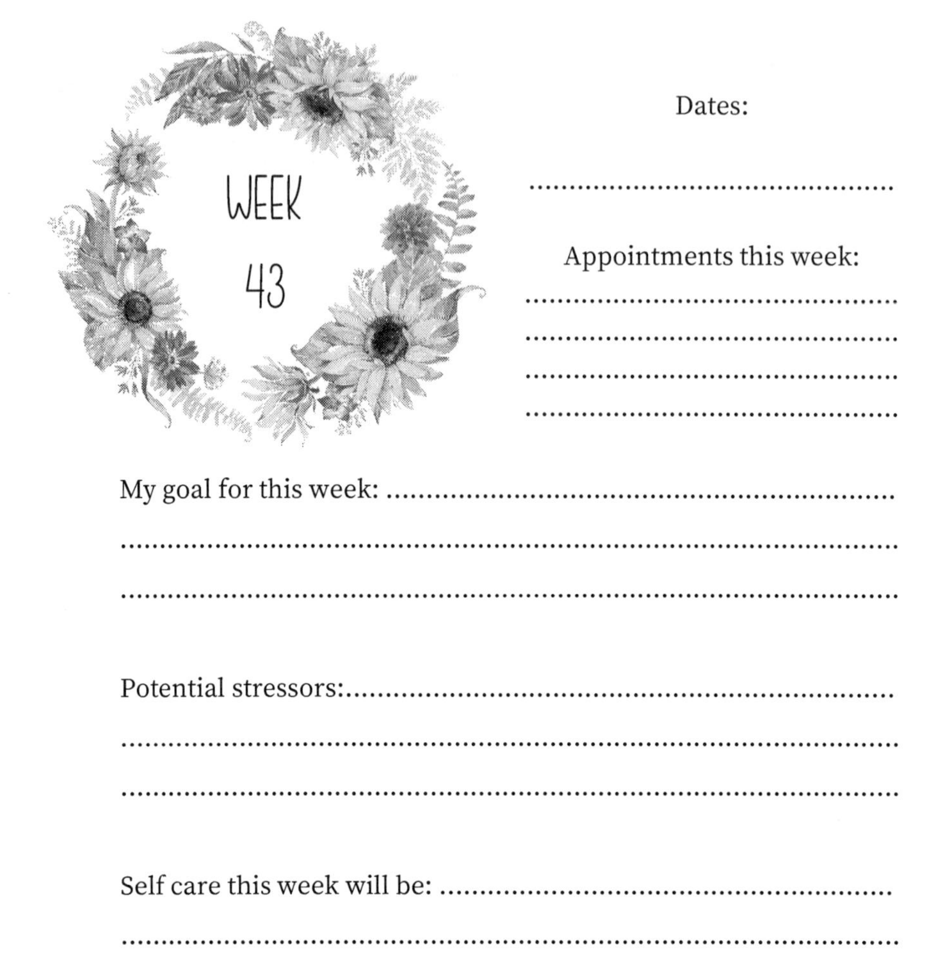

Dates:

....

Appointments this week:

....

....

....

....

My goal for this week: ....

....

....

Potential stressors:..

....

....

Self care this week will be: ....

....

....

Plan for including physical fitness: ....

....

....

Plan for healthy eating: ....

....

....

Hobbies or interests I will pursue this week: ....

....

This week, I plan to reach out to: ....

....

Sleep goal: .... hours each night

Monday

I slept	I ate (circle)	I spent
hours	1 2 3 healthy meals	minutes on self care or hobbies
I reached out to	Today I feel/felt	Today's positive moment

Tuesday

I slept	I ate (circle)	I spent
hours	1 2 3 healthy meals	minutes on self care or hobbies
I reached out to	Today I feel/felt	Today's positive moment

Wednesday

I slept hours	I ate (circle) 1 2 3 healthy meals	I spent minutes on self care or hobbies
I reached out to	Today I feel/felt	Today's positive moment

Thursday

I slept hours	I ate (circle) 1 2 3 healthy meals	I spent minutes on self care or hobbies
I reached out to	Today I feel/felt	Today's positive moment

Friday

I slept hours	I ate (circle) 1 2 3 healthy meals	I spent minutes on self care or hobbies
I reached out to	Today I feel/felt	Today's positive moment

Saturday

I slept	I ate (circle)	I spent
hours	1 2 3 healthy meals	minutes on self care or hobbies
I reached out to	Today I feel/felt	Today's positive moment

Sunday

I slept	I ate (circle)	I spent
hours	1 2 3 healthy meals	minutes on self care or hobbies
I reached out to	Today I feel/felt	Today's positive moment

WEEKLY REFLECTION

How did you do this week with taking care of yourself?

....

....

....

....

....

....

Dates:

....

Appointments this week:

....

....

....

....

My goal for this week: ....

....

....

Potential stressors:..

....

....

Self care this week will be: ....

....

....

Plan for including physical fitness: ....

....

....

Plan for healthy eating: ....

....

....

Hobbies or interests I will pursue this week: ....

....

This week, I plan to reach out to: ....

....

Sleep goal: .... hours each night

Monday

I slept	I ate (circle)	I spent
hours	1 2 3 healthy meals	minutes on self care or hobbies
I reached out to	Today I feel/felt	Today's positive moment

Tuesday

I slept	I ate (circle)	I spent
hours	1 2 3 healthy meals	minutes on self care or hobbies
I reached out to	Today I feel/felt	Today's positive moment

Wednesday

I slept	I ate (circle)	I spent
hours	1 2 3 healthy meals	minutes on self care or hobbies
I reached out to	Today I feel/felt	Today's positive moment

Thursday

I slept	I ate (circle)	I spent
hours	1 2 3 healthy meals	minutes on self care or hobbies
I reached out to	Today I feel/felt	Today's positive moment

Friday

I slept	I ate (circle)	I spent
hours	1 2 3 healthy meals	minutes on self care or hobbies
I reached out to	Today I feel/felt	Today's positive moment

Saturday

I slept	I ate (circle)	I spent
hours	1 2 3 healthy meals	minutes on self care or hobbies
I reached out to	Today I feel/felt	Today's positive moment

Sunday

I slept	I ate (circle)	I spent
hours	1 2 3 healthy meals	minutes on self care or hobbies
I reached out to	Today I feel/felt	Today's positive moment

WEEKLY REFLECTION

How did you do this week with taking care of yourself?

....

....

....

....

....

....

MONTHY REFLECTION

I was/was not able to meet my main goal this month because:

....

....

....

The schedule I set for myself was helpful/ needs work and I will:

....

....

....

This month I spent time taking care of my physical health by:

....

....

I feel my sleep habits were:

....

....

My diet this month can be best described as:

....

....

This month, my self-care looked like:

....

....

....

This month, I reached out to:

....

....

This month, I made time to rest and enjoy my hobbies by:

....

....

....

The most stressful moment of the month was:

....

....

....

The best memory of the month was:

....

....

....

....

....

....

Emotional and mental health are often overlooked when caring for others. We tend to put ourselves on the back burner and only address our needs when we are facing burnout. Journaling, counseling, and support groups are fantastic for supporting you on this journey. Identify counseling services and community support groups that are available in the event you need additional support. These services are for YOU, not your loved one. How will you care for your emotional and mental health?

....

....

....

....

....

....

....

....

....

....

....

....

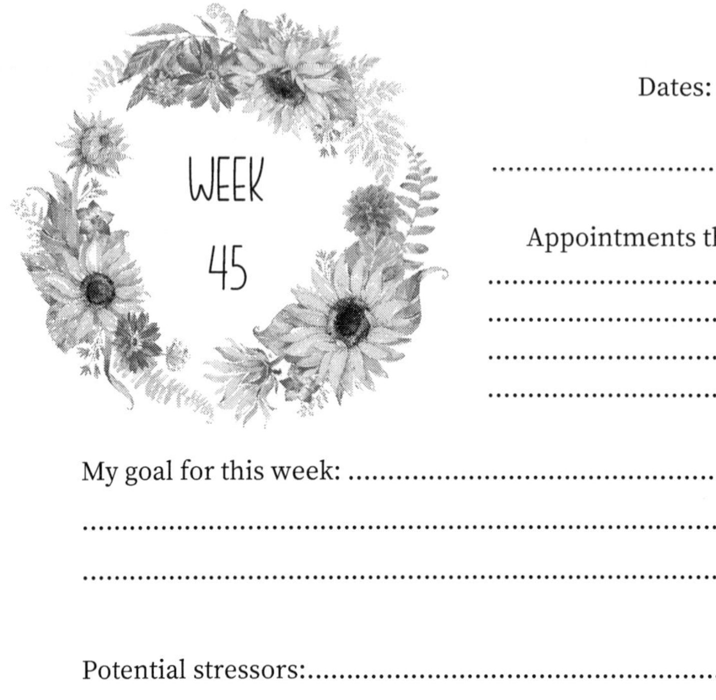

Dates:

....

Appointments this week:

....

....

....

....

My goal for this week: ....

....

....

Potential stressors:...

....

....

Self care this week will be: ....

....

....

Plan for including physical fitness: ....

....

....

Plan for healthy eating: ....

....

....

Hobbies or interests I will pursue this week: ....

....

This week, I plan to reach out to: ....

....

Sleep goal: .... hours each night

Monday

I slept	I ate (circle)	I spent
hours	1 2 3 healthy meals	minutes on self care or hobbies
I reached out to	Today I feel/felt	Today's positive moment

Tuesday

I slept	I ate (circle)	I spent
hours	1 2 3 healthy meals	minutes on self care or hobbies
I reached out to	Today I feel/felt	Today's positive moment

Wednesday

I slept	I ate (circle)	I spent
hours	1 2 3 healthy meals	minutes on self care or hobbies
I reached out to	Today I feel/felt	Today's positive moment

Thursday

I slept	I ate (circle)	I spent
hours	1 2 3 healthy meals	minutes on self care or hobbies
I reached out to	Today I feel/felt	Today's positive moment

Friday

I slept	I ate (circle)	I spent
hours	1 2 3 healthy meals	minutes on self care or hobbies
I reached out to	Today I feel/felt	Today's positive moment

Saturday

I slept	I ate (circle)	I spent
hours	1 2 3 healthy meals	minutes on self care or hobbies
I reached out to	Today I feel/felt	Today's positive moment

Sunday

I slept	I ate (circle)	I spent
hours	1 2 3 healthy meals	minutes on self care or hobbies
I reached out to	Today I feel/felt	Today's positive moment

WEEKLY REFLECTION

How did you do this week with taking care of yourself?

....

....

....

....

....

....

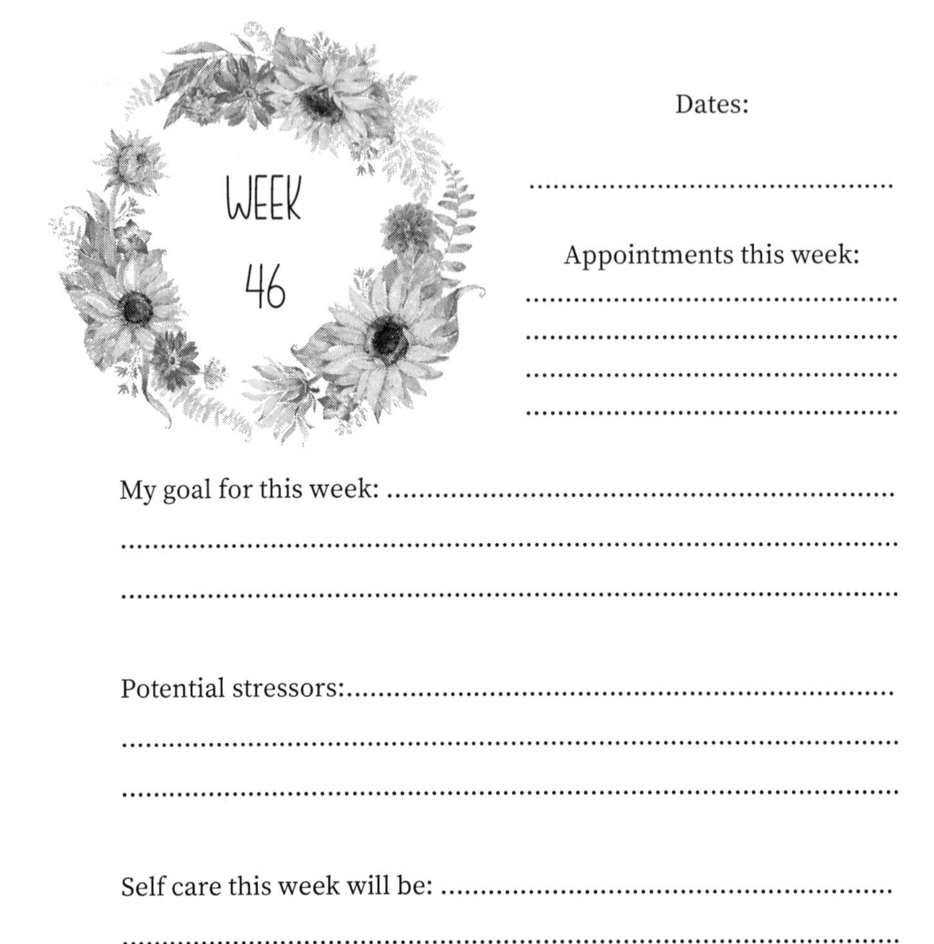

Dates:

....

Appointments this week:

....

....

....

....

My goal for this week: ....

....

....

Potential stressors: ....

....

....

Self care this week will be: ....

....

....

Plan for including physical fitness: ....

....

....

Plan for healthy eating: ....

....

....

Hobbies or interests I will pursue this week: ....
....

This week, I plan to reach out to: ....
....

Sleep goal: .... hours each night

Monday

I slept	I ate (circle)	I spent
hours	1 2 3 healthy meals	minutes on self care or hobbies
I reached out to	Today I feel/felt	Today's positive moment

Tuesday

I slept	I ate (circle)	I spent
hours	1 2 3 healthy meals	minutes on self care or hobbies
I reached out to	Today I feel/felt	Today's positive moment

Wednesday

I slept	I ate (circle)	I spent
hours	1 2 3 healthy meals	minutes on self care or hobbies
I reached out to	Today I feel/felt	Today's positive moment

Thursday

I slept	I ate (circle)	I spent
hours	1 2 3 healthy meals	minutes on self care or hobbies
I reached out to	Today I feel/felt	Today's positive moment

Friday

I slept	I ate (circle)	I spent
hours	1 2 3 healthy meals	minutes on self care or hobbies
I reached out to	Today I feel/felt	Today's positive moment

Saturday

I slept	I ate (circle)	I spent
hours	1 2 3 healthy meals	minutes on self care or hobbies

I reached out to	Today I feel/felt	Today's positive moment

Sunday

I slept	I ate (circle)	I spent
hours	1 2 3 healthy meals	minutes on self care or hobbies

I reached out to	Today I feel/felt	Today's positive moment

WEEKLY REFLECTION

How did you do this week with taking care of yourself?

....

....

....

....

....

....

Dates:

....

Appointments this week:

....

....

....

....

My goal for this week: ....

....

....

Potential stressors:...

....

....

Self care this week will be: ....

....

....

Plan for including physical fitness: ....

....

....

Plan for healthy eating: ....

....

....

Hobbies or interests I will pursue this week: ....

....

This week, I plan to reach out to: ....

....

Sleep goal: .... hours each night

Monday

I slept	I ate (circle)	I spent
hours	1 2 3 healthy meals	minutes on self care or hobbies
I reached out to	Today I feel/felt	Today's positive moment

Tuesday

I slept	I ate (circle)	I spent
hours	1 2 3 healthy meals	minutes on self care or hobbies
I reached out to	Today I feel/felt	Today's positive moment

Wednesday

I slept	I ate (circle)	I spent
hours	1 2 3 healthy meals	minutes on self care or hobbies
I reached out to	Today I feel/felt	Today's positive moment

Thursday

I slept	I ate (circle)	I spent
hours	1 2 3 healthy meals	minutes on self care or hobbies
I reached out to	Today I feel/felt	Today's positive moment

Friday

I slept	I ate (circle)	I spent
hours	1 2 3 healthy meals	minutes on self care or hobbies
I reached out to	Today I feel/felt	Today's positive moment

Saturday

I slept	I ate (circle)	I spent
hours	1 2 3 healthy meals	minutes on self care or hobbies
I reached out to	Today I feel/felt	Today's positive moment

Sunday

I slept	I ate (circle)	I spent
hours	1 2 3 healthy meals	minutes on self care or hobbies
I reached out to	Today I feel/felt	Today's positive moment

WEEKLY REFLECTION

How did you do this week with taking care of yourself?

....

....

....

....

....

....

Dates:

....

Appointments this week:

....

....

....

....

My goal for this week: ....

....

....

Potential stressors:...

....

....

Self care this week will be: ....

....

....

Plan for including physical fitness: ....

....

....

Plan for healthy eating: ....

....

....

Hobbies or interests I will pursue this week: ....

....

This week, I plan to reach out to: ....

....

Sleep goal: .... hours each night

Monday

I slept	I ate (circle)	I spent
hours	1 2 3 healthy meals	minutes on self care or hobbies
I reached out to	Today I feel/felt	Today's positive moment

Tuesday

I slept	I ate (circle)	I spent
hours	1 2 3 healthy meals	minutes on self care or hobbies
I reached out to	Today I feel/felt	Today's positive moment

Wednesday

I slept	I ate (circle)	I spent
hours	1 2 3 healthy meals	minutes on self care or hobbies
I reached out to	Today I feel/felt	Today's positive moment

Thursday

I slept	I ate (circle)	I spent
hours	1 2 3 healthy meals	minutes on self care or hobbies
I reached out to	Today I feel/felt	Today's positive moment

Friday

I slept	I ate (circle)	I spent
hours	1 2 3 healthy meals	minutes on self care or hobbies
I reached out to	Today I feel/felt	Today's positive moment

Saturday

I slept	I ate (circle)	I spent
hours	1 2 3 healthy meals	minutes on self care or hobbies
I reached out to	Today I feel/felt	Today's positive moment

Sunday

I slept	I ate (circle)	I spent
hours	1 2 3 healthy meals	minutes on self care or hobbies
I reached out to	Today I feel/felt	Today's positive moment

WEEKLY REFLECTION

How did you do this week with taking care of yourself?

....

....

....

....

....

....

MONTHY REFLECTION

I was/was not able to meet my main goal this month because:

....

....

....

The schedule I set for myself was helpful/ needs work and I will:

....

....

....

This month I spent time taking care of my physical health by:

....

....

I feel my sleep habits were:

....

....

My diet this month can be best described as:

....

....

This month, my self-care looked like:

....

....

....

This month, I reached out to:

....

....

This month, I made time to rest and enjoy my hobbies by:

....

....

....

The most stressful moment of the month was:

....

....

....

The best memory of the month was:

....

....

....

....

....

....

Family traditions bring joy to people as we celebrate different holidays. Take some time to reflect on your own family traditions and what annual routines bring you happiness. Write down your family's traditions in the space below.

....

....

....

....

....

....

....

....

....

....

....

....

....

....

....

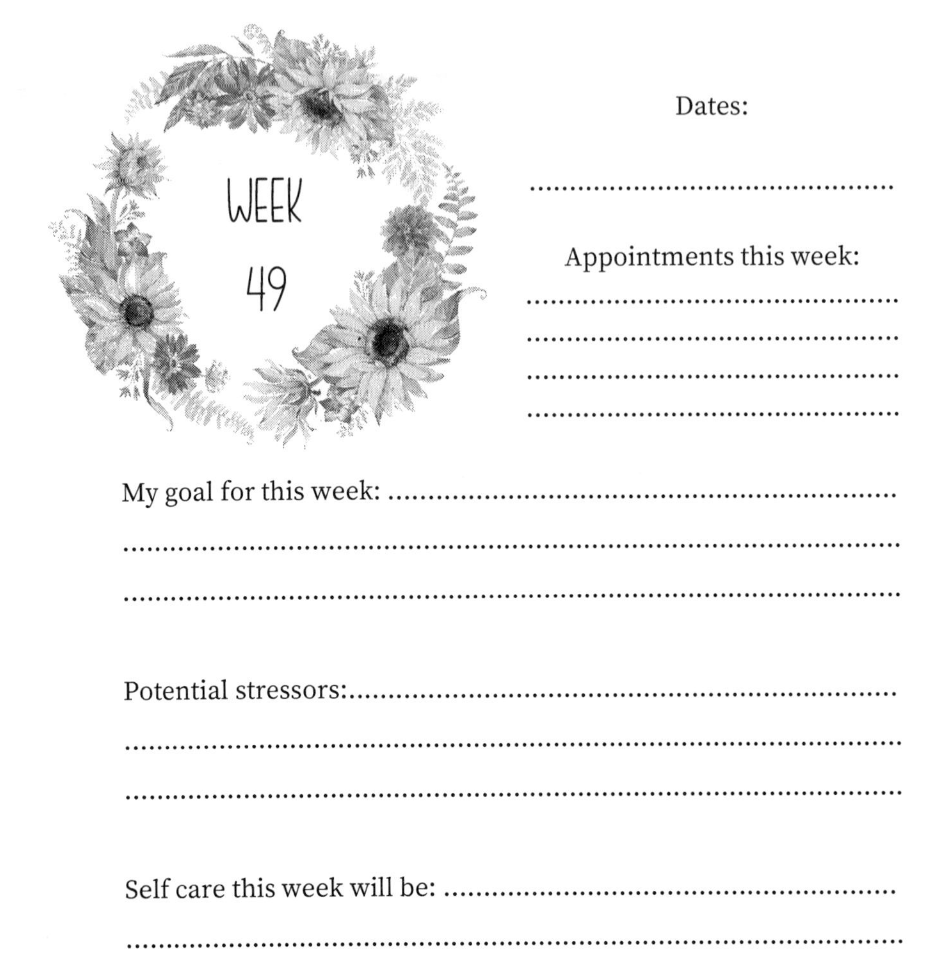

Dates:

....

Appointments this week:

....

....

....

....

My goal for this week: ....

....

....

Potential stressors:...

....

....

Self care this week will be: ....

....

....

Plan for including physical fitness: ....

....

....

Plan for healthy eating: ....

....

....

Hobbies or interests I will pursue this week: ....

....

This week, I plan to reach out to: ....

....

Sleep goal: .... hours each night

Monday

I slept	I ate (circle)	I spent
hours	1 2 3 healthy meals	minutes on self care or hobbies
I reached out to	Today I feel/felt	Today's positive moment

Tuesday

I slept	I ate (circle)	I spent
hours	1 2 3 healthy meals	minutes on self care or hobbies
I reached out to	Today I feel/felt	Today's positive moment

Wednesday

I slept	I ate (circle)	I spent
hours	1 2 3 healthy meals	minutes on self care or hobbies
I reached out to	Today I feel/felt	Today's positive moment

Thursday

I slept	I ate (circle)	I spent
hours	1 2 3 healthy meals	minutes on self care or hobbies
I reached out to	Today I feel/felt	Today's positive moment

Friday

I slept	I ate (circle)	I spent
hours	1 2 3 healthy meals	minutes on self care or hobbies
I reached out to	Today I feel/felt	Today's positive moment

Saturday

I slept	I ate (circle)	I spent
hours	1 2 3 healthy meals	minutes on self care or hobbies
I reached out to	Today I feel/felt	Today's positive moment

Sunday

I slept	I ate (circle)	I spent
hours	1 2 3 healthy meals	minutes on self care or hobbies
I reached out to	Today I feel/felt	Today's positive moment

WEEKLY REFLECTION

How did you do this week with taking care of yourself?

....

....

....

....

....

....

Dates:

....

Appointments this week:

....

....

....

....

My goal for this week: ....

....

....

Potential stressors:..

....

....

Self care this week will be: ....

....

....

Plan for including physical fitness: ....

....

....

Plan for healthy eating: ....

....

....

Hobbies or interests I will pursue this week: ....

....

This week, I plan to reach out to: ....

....

Sleep goal: .... hours each night

Monday

I slept	I ate (circle)	I spent
hours	1 2 3 healthy meals	minutes on self care or hobbies
I reached out to	Today I feel/felt	Today's positive moment

Tuesday

I slept	I ate (circle)	I spent
hours	1 2 3 healthy meals	minutes on self care or hobbies
I reached out to	Today I feel/felt	Today's positive moment

Wednesday

I slept hours	I ate (circle) 1 2 3 healthy meals	I spent minutes on self care or hobbies
I reached out to	Today I feel/felt	Today's positive moment

Thursday

I slept hours	I ate (circle) 1 2 3 healthy meals	I spent minutes on self care or hobbies
I reached out to	Today I feel/felt	Today's positive moment

Friday

I slept hours	I ate (circle) 1 2 3 healthy meals	I spent minutes on self care or hobbies
I reached out to	Today I feel/felt	Today's positive moment

Saturday

I slept	I ate (circle)	I spent
hours	1 2 3 healthy meals	minutes on self care or hobbies
I reached out to	Today I feel/felt	Today's positive moment

Sunday

I slept	I ate (circle)	I spent
hours	1 2 3 healthy meals	minutes on self care or hobbies
I reached out to	Today I feel/felt	Today's positive moment

WEEKLY REFLECTION

How did you do this week with taking care of yourself?

....

....

....

....

....

....

Dates:

....

Appointments this week:

....

....

....

....

My goal for this week: ....

....

....

Potential stressors:...

....

....

Self care this week will be: ....

....

....

Plan for including physical fitness: ....

....

....

Plan for healthy eating: ....

....

....

Hobbies or interests I will pursue this week: ....
....

This week, I plan to reach out to: ....
....

Sleep goal: .... hours each night

Monday

I slept hours	I ate (circle) 1 2 3 healthy meals	I spent minutes on self care or hobbies
I reached out to	Today I feel/felt	Today's positive moment

Tuesday

I slept hours	I ate (circle) 1 2 3 healthy meals	I spent minutes on self care or hobbies
I reached out to	Today I feel/felt	Today's positive moment

Wednesday

I slept	I ate (circle)	I spent
hours	1 2 3 healthy meals	minutes on self care or hobbies

I reached out to	Today I feel/felt	Today's positive moment

Thursday

I slept	I ate (circle)	I spent
hours	1 2 3 healthy meals	minutes on self care or hobbies

I reached out to	Today I feel/felt	Today's positive moment

Friday

I slept	I ate (circle)	I spent
hours	1 2 3 healthy meals	minutes on self care or hobbies

I reached out to	Today I feel/felt	Today's positive moment

Saturday

I slept	I ate (circle)	I spent
hours	1 2 3 healthy meals	minutes on self care or hobbies
I reached out to	Today I feel/felt	Today's positive moment

Sunday

I slept	I ate (circle)	I spent
hours	1 2 3 healthy meals	minutes on self care or hobbies
I reached out to	Today I feel/felt	Today's positive moment

WEEKLY REFLECTION

How did you do this week with taking care of yourself?

....

....

....

....

....

....

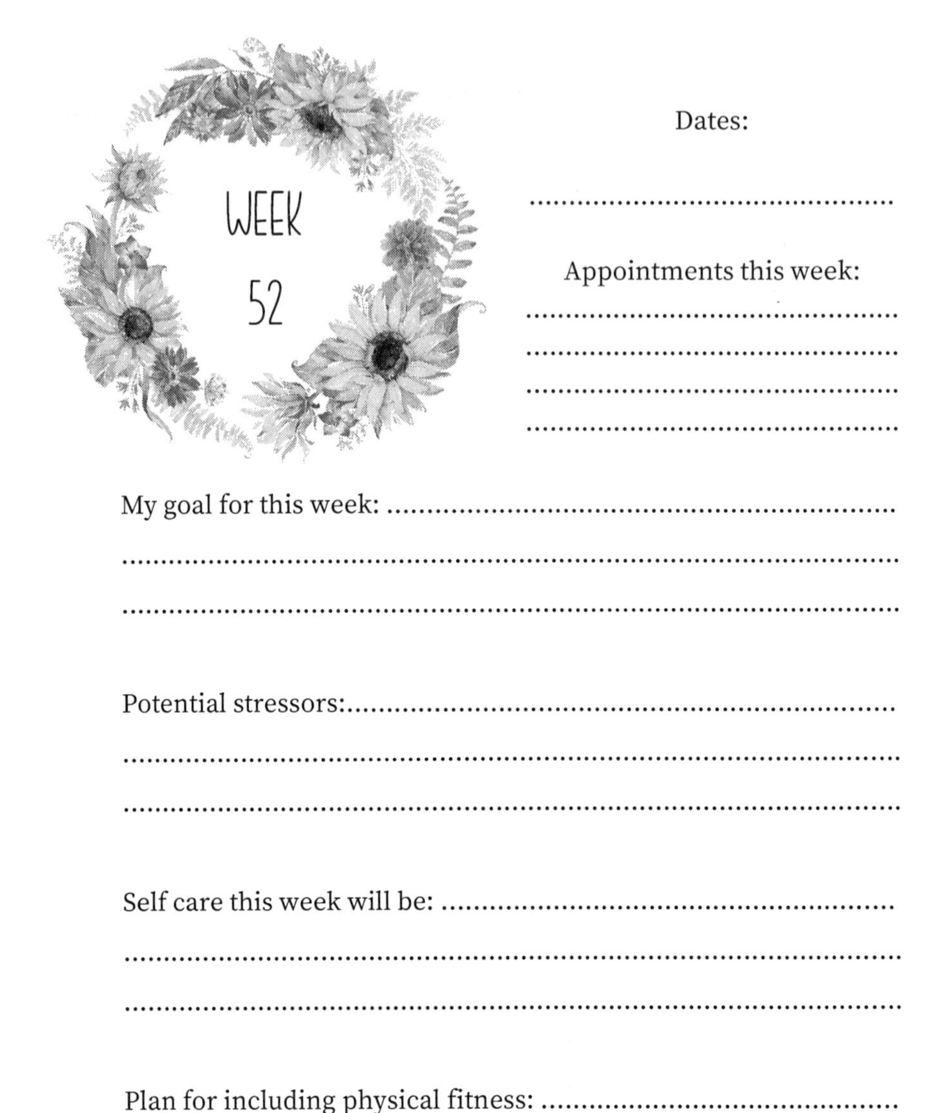

Dates:

Appointments this week:

My goal for this week:

Potential stressors:

Self care this week will be:

Plan for including physical fitness:

Plan for healthy eating:

Hobbies or interests I will pursue this week: ....
....

This week, I plan to reach out to: ....
....

Sleep goal: .... hours each night

Monday

I slept	I ate (circle)	I spent
hours	1 2 3 healthy meals	minutes on self care or hobbies
I reached out to	Today I feel/felt	Today's positive moment

Tuesday

I slept	I ate (circle)	I spent
hours	1 2 3 healthy meals	minutes on self care or hobbies
I reached out to	Today I feel/felt	Today's positive moment

Wednesday

I slept	I ate (circle)	I spent
hours	1 2 3 healthy meals	minutes on self care or hobbies

I reached out to	Today I feel/felt	Today's positive moment

Thursday

I slept	I ate (circle)	I spent
hours	1 2 3 healthy meals	minutes on self care or hobbies

I reached out to	Today I feel/felt	Today's positive moment

Friday

I slept	I ate (circle)	I spent
hours	1 2 3 healthy meals	minutes on self care or hobbies

I reached out to	Today I feel/felt	Today's positive moment

Saturday

I slept	I ate (circle)	I spent
hours	1 2 3 healthy meals	minutes on self care or hobbies
I reached out to	Today I feel/felt	Today's positive moment

Sunday

I slept	I ate (circle)	I spent
hours	1 2 3 healthy meals	minutes on self care or hobbies
I reached out to	Today I feel/felt	Today's positive moment

WEEKLY REFLECTION

How did you do this week with taking care of yourself?

....

....

....

....

....

....

MONTHY REFLECTION

I was/was not able to meet my main goal this month because:

....

....

....

The schedule I set for myself was helpful/ needs work and I will:

....

....

....

This month I spent time taking care of my physical health by:

....

....

I feel my sleep habits were:

....

....

My diet this month can be best described as:

....

....

This month, my self-care looked like:

This month, I reached out to:

This month, I made time to rest and enjoy my hobbies by:

The most stressful moment of the month was:

The best memory of the month was:

CLOSING REFLECTION QUESTIONS

The most memorable moments of the last year are:

....

....

....

....

Things I learned about myself:

....

....

....

....

Things I learned about my loved one:

....

....

....

....

Ways I struggled to care for myself:

....

....

....

....

CLOSING REFLECTION QUESTIONS

Ways I struggled to care for my loved one:

....

....

....

....

How I plan to care for myself better in the coming year:

....

....

....

....

People who helped me care for myself and my loved one:

....

....

....

....

How I plan to get assistance for the following year:

....

....

....

....

CLOSING REFLECTION QUESTIONS

What I enjoyed about being a caregiver for my loved one:

....

....

....

....

Things I found difficult about being a caregiver for my loved one:

....

....

....

....

My goals for the following year are:

....

....

....

....

....

....

....

....

....

....

CLOSING REFLECTION QUESTIONS

Other thoughts:

OTHER FOCUS JOURNALS BY ORANGE BLOSSOM

Creatives' Journal for Inspiration and Productivity

Mothers' Journal for Inner Peace

The Believer's Journal for Everyday Faith

Chronic Pain Journal for Calm

Teachers' Journal for Balance

From Burnout to Balance: A Nursing Resilience Journal

www.OrangeBlossomBooks.com

Made in United States
Orlando, FL
09 July 2023